THE HOME WORKSHOP SERIES

THE WOOD-TURNING LATHE

RAY E. HAINES • JOHN V. ADAMS • JOHN G. MILLER
ROBERT L. THOMPSON • RAYMOND VAN TASSEL
Department of Vocational Education, New York University

D. VAN NOSTRAND COMPANY, INC.
NEW YORK • TORONTO • LONDON

NEW YORK

D. Van Nostrand Company, Inc., 250 Fourth Avenue, New York 3

TORONTO

D. Van Nostrand Company (Canada), Ltd., 228 Bloor Street, Toronto

LONDON

Macmillan & Company, Ltd., St. Martin's Street, London, W.C. 2

PRINTED IN THE UNITED STATES OF AMERICA

Preface

A knowledge of the wood-turning lathe and skill in its operation are especially useful for the home craftsman or the operator of power tools. It is the purpose of this book to provide this knowledge and to present safe and skillful techniques as well as to illustrate a variety of projects that can be made with the wood-turning lathe.

The material in this book is organized so that the reader first becomes familiar with the wood-turning lathe itself: its construction and principle of operation; the gouges and chisels and the many accessories of the lathe; and the care and maintenance of both the lathe and its tools. Then the operations that can be performed on the lathe are explained, proceeding from the basic ones, such as turning a cylinder, on to the more advanced, such as chuck turning. Illustrations that emphasize proper technique are used frequently to supplement the written explanations. Finally the projects are presented. Bills of materials, plan drawings, and explanatory procedure are given which are the result of shop experience. Pictures are used so that finished articles can be visualized.

In order to assure the legibility of the book while the reader works under shop conditions, a large page with large type has been chosen. An attempt has been made to place the explanatory procedure of the project side by side with the appropriate plan drawings wherever possible. Thus, when the book lies open, it is hoped that the reader will find great convenience while he works on a particular project explained in this book.

Acknowledgment is made to Mr. Elliott Polansky for the preparation of the drawings. Mr. Polansky stepped in most co-operatively to replace Mr. Carlton Bauer, who was recalled to active duty in the Armed Forces.

R. E. H.

Contents

I

History and Basic Principle of the Lathe

A lathe is a machine which is used to produce cylindrical, conical, or other circular forms from many different kinds of materials (Fig. 1-1). A lathe which has been made for the purpose of producing work in wood is known as a *wood-turning lathe*. The operation of removing material from the rotating piece with a sharp-edged tool is known as *turning*.

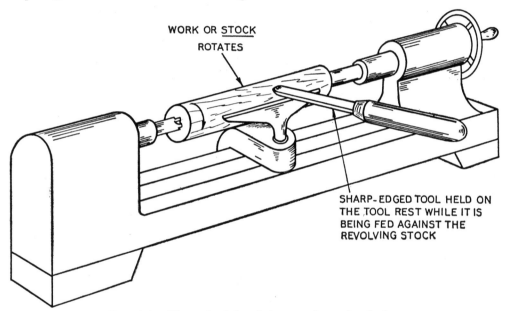

FIG. 1-1   The principle of the wood-turning lathe.

The work, or *stock* as it is sometimes called, is fastened to the rotating member of the lathe and is revolved at a fairly high rate of speed. A sharp-edged tool is held in one hand and steadied on the tool rest by the other while it is fed or pressed into the revolving work. The action of the tool as it contacts the work produces shavings, and the work takes the form of a cylinder, cone, or other surface of revolution.

The earliest lathe was a simple machine made to support the ends of the work on centers (Fig. 1-2). These centers were pointed projections of hard wood which had been fastened to each of two trees. The work piece was rotated by means of a rope, one end of which was fastened to an overhanging limb. The rope was then wound around the work two or three times, and a loop was placed

1

in the other end. Either the operator or his helper placed his foot in the looped end of the rope and produced an alternate back-and-forth motion of the work by moving his foot up and down. The operator, or *turner* as he was called, held a sharp chisel, supported on a wooden tool rest, which was made by fastening a strip of wood between the trees at about the height of the lathe centers. When the rotation of the work was in the direction of the operator, he pressed

FIG. 1-2   Early tree lathe.

the chisel against the work, thus taking a cut off the stock. During the return stroke, the operator withdrew his chisel, thus allowing the tree limb to return the work to the original position.

A further development of this original principle was incorporated in the *spring pole lathe* which was an indoor machine of smaller dimensions than the tree lathe. The spring pole lathe was used extensively up to the time of the Industrial Revolution. This old lathe was constructed of heavy timbers bolted together to form the *bed* of the machine. The centers were secured in two upright members, one of which was adjustable for work of varying lengths. A treadle replaced the loop used in the tree lathe, and a flexible pole, fastened to the ceiling, took the place of the limb of the tree. The turner would press down on the treadle and move his turning tool against the rotating work. When he released pressure on the treadle, the pole would snap back and the work would rotate in the opposite direction. The turner, therefore, could cut only during half the time of operation.

FIG. 1-3   The wheel lathe.

FIG. 1-4   The treadle lathe.

Smaller lathes with the same alternate motion were powered by the means of a bow string wound around the work piece. The rotation of the work was then produced by moving the bow to-and-fro with one hand while the turning tool was manipulated with the other. Lathes of this type were used by the Egyptians as early as 740 B.C. and are still in use today by craftsmen in many parts of the world.

Continuous rotation of the spindle was the next step in the development of the turning lathe. During the 15th century the French, who were known for the quality of their wood turning, used a lathe which was given continuous rotation through the use of a "great wheel" mounted behind the lathe (Fig. 1-3).

Lathes used by the craftsman of about one hundred years ago were of the treadle type being made either of wood or metal (Fig. 1-4). It was held by some that a machine of this type, when constructed of metal, lacked the ability to absorb the vibrations caused by the "high" speeds. Wooden construction cushioned some of this undesirable vibration.

Improvements in the modern lathe include higher and more convenient selection of work speeds made possible by the use of the electric motor as a means of power. The use of new metal alloys, improvement in efficiency of bearings, coupled with modern mass production methods, have made possible a high-quality machine within the price range of one who might be interested in wood-turning as a hobby.

II

The Home Workshop Lathe

Before starting work on the lathe, the worker should be familiar with the parts of the lathe and the function of each part. The basic principle of operation and the basic parts are the same for all wood-turning lathes. Each manufacturer usually stresses certain features which may make his lathe slightly different from the others. It is the purpose of this section to familiarize the owner or prospective owner of a wood-turning lathe with the function of the basic parts and with the special features wherein various makes of lathe may differ in appearance and in operation.

Fig. 2-1 illustrates the basic parts of all wood-turning lathes. The wood is shaped by holding a cutting tool against it while it revolves between two centers. The centers must be supported in such a position that pieces of wood of various sizes may turn freely. As the worker faces the lathe, the center on the left is called the live center, or the spur center. This center is generally inserted in a hollow spindle which is supported by suitable bearings. The end of the spindle is usually threaded to hold a face plate for face-plate turning. The spindle and bearings are fastened in the headstock which is bolted securely to the bed of the lathe. The spindle is rotated by a motor, usually through a V-belt and pulley. Most lathes are equipped with a means for feeding a lubricant, either oil or grease, to the bearings. The worker must be sure to keep these bearings well lubricated.

On the right of the operator is the dead center, or cup center. This center is inserted in a spindle which is supported by the tailstock. The tail spindle can be moved in and out of the tailstock by turning the hand wheel on the end of the spindle. The spindle can be locked securely in position with the spindle clamp. The tailstock may be slid along the ways of the bed and locked in position with the tailstock clamp to accommodate various lengths of stock.

The tool rest and tool-rest holder are clamped to the bed of the lathe in any required position between the headstock and the tailstock. The tool rest offers support to the cutting tools as they are guided into the stock by the operator.

Some lathe beds are provided with legs which make the lathe a floor model, while others without legs may be bolted securely to a bench top.

The motor mounting may be in different locations on various lathes. The headstock spindle of most lathes revolves at speeds ranging from 350 to 3400 revolutions per minute, depending on the size and number of steps on the pulleys and

5

the speed of the motor. Most wood-turning should be performed within this range of speeds.

The size of a lathe is indicated by the swing of the lathe and by the maximum length of stock that can be turned between centers. By the "swing of the lathe," we mean the maximum diameter of the stock that can be turned. If the distance

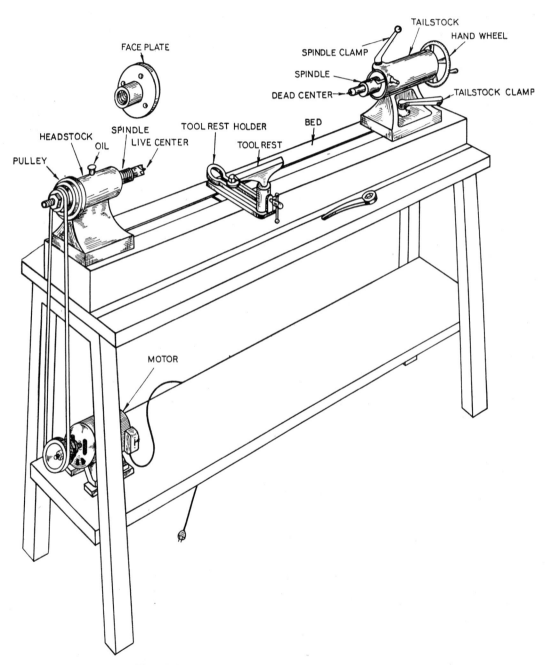

FIG. 2-1   Basic parts of a wood-turning lathe.

FIG. 2-2   Headstock with pulley enclosed.

measured from the ways of the lathe to the point of the center is 5″, then a piece of stock 10″ in diameter can be turned on the lathe. It is then indicated that this is a 10″ lathe. A satisfactory lathe for home work-shops has a 12″ swing and measures 36″ or more between centers.

The worker must assume the responsibility for oil-ing all moving parts and for keeping the lathe clean and free from wood chips and dust, hardened oil, and finishing materials that may drip on the bed of the lathe during the finishing process.

FIG. 2-3   Indexing device.

Many of the late models of lathes are equipped with a headstock that has the pulley enclosed (Fig. 2-2). This adds to the rigidity of the spindle support. An-

FIG. 2-4   Motor built in headstock.

other feature of some small lathes is the indexing device which is shown in Fig. 2-3. This device is helpful when laying out a spindle turning for fluting and reeding (see p. 43 for use of this device). It can be noted that the spindle of this model is threaded on both ends to accommodate a face plate on either end.

Several manufacturers feature a variable-speed device for controlling spindle speeds. Other lathes can be purchased with a motor built into the headstock. (Fig. 2-4).

III

Basic Tools and Accessories: Their Use and Care

The Tools. The basic tools used by the wood-turner are shown in Figs. 3-1 and 3-2. Tools (a) and (b) in Fig. 3-1 are gouges. These are used for spindle turning (turning between centers) when reducing the stock to a cylindrical shape and for concave cuts, or circular grooves. Gouges may also be used when doing

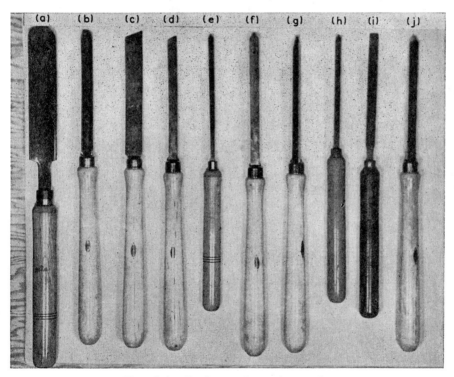

FIG. 3-1 Basic wood-turning tools.

face-plate turning for roughing down the piece of stock to shape. Gouges may be purchased in sizes (which are measured across the width) from $\frac{1}{4}''$ to $2''$ or larger. The $\frac{1}{2}''$ and the $1\frac{1}{4}''$ sizes are suitable for the beginner.

Tools (c) and (d) in Fig. 3-1 are called skew chisels. The cutting edge is ground at an angle of approximately 70 degrees with the long side of the chisel. Although the ground sides of the chisel are flat when purchased, they should be shaped to

9

a convex surface similar to an ax. The most handy type of skew chisel is one that is ground with a bevel on both sides of the blade. This tool is used for smoothing the surfaces of stock which has been reduced to approximately the desired size, for making V-cuts, convex cuts (beads), and for trimming ends and square shoulders. Skew chisels may be purchased in sizes ranging from $\frac{1}{8}''$ to $1\frac{1}{2}''$ or larger. The $\frac{1}{2}''$ and the $1\frac{1}{4}''$ sizes are suitable for beginners.

Tools (e) and (f) in Fig. 3-1 are called round-nose chisels and are used for forming and for smoothing grooves and concave recesses in either spindle turning

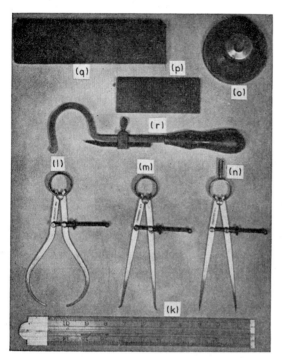

FIG. 3 2   Basic wood-turning tools.

or face-plate turning. Round-nose chisels may be purchased in sizes ranging from $\frac{1}{8}''$ to $1\frac{1}{4}''$ or larger, but the beginner can get along well with a $\frac{1}{4}''$ and a $\frac{1}{2}''$ size.

Tool (g) illustrated in Fig. 3-1 is called a parting tool and is used for cutting recesses or grooves with flat sides and a flat bottom. The bevel is ground on both sides. A rib usually extends the entire length of the blade down the center of each side. The width of the parting tool is measured through the thickness of the blade, or from the rib on one side to the rib on the other side. This tool may be purchased in sizes ranging from $\frac{1}{8}''$ to $\frac{3}{4}''$, but the $\frac{3}{16}''$ size is suitable for the beginner.

The square-nose chisel is illustrated as (h) and (i) in Fig. 3-1. It is shaped similar to a regular woodworking chisel and is used for making square shoulders and flat-bottomed cuts. A $\frac{1}{4}''$ and a $\frac{1}{2}''$ square-nosed tool is suitable for most lathe work.

The diamond-point or spear-point tool is shown as tool (j) in Fig. 3-1. This tool is used for making V-cuts and for rounding beads. It is ground at an included angle of approximately 60° so that the point is formed in the center. A $\frac{1}{2}''$ or a $\frac{3}{4}''$ diamond-point chisel is a suitable size.

Some wood-turners have preferences for sizes different from those suggested, and the worker may find, after gaining some experience, that he will desire to obtain additional sizes in some or all of these tools.

Measuring and laying out are done with a rule such as the one shown in (k) of Fig. 3-2. The one illustrated here is a 2-foot folding rule which is a handy size for lathe work.

The calipers shown in (l) and (m) of Fig. 3-2 are used for checking the diameters of the stock being shaped. The outside caliper (l) is used for checking diameters of cylindrical work and the inside caliper (m) is used for checking the diameter of a hole when doing face-plate boring. Calipers may be purchased in various sizes, but the 6″ size is handy for the beginner. The dividers shown as (n) in Fig. 3-2 are used for laying out distances on the stock.

A suitable oil-can (o, Fig. 3-2) is necessary for lubricating the moving parts of the machine and for lubricating the dead center as well as for applying oil to the sharpening tools. The slipstone illustrated as (p) in Fig. 3-2 is necessary for sharpening gouges. These may be purchased in a variety of sizes and grades, but a medium-grade India stone $4\frac{1}{2}$″ long, $1\frac{3}{4}$″ wide with a $\frac{1}{2}$″ back and a $\frac{3}{16}$″ edge will be suitable for sharpening the gouges suggested for the beginner. A

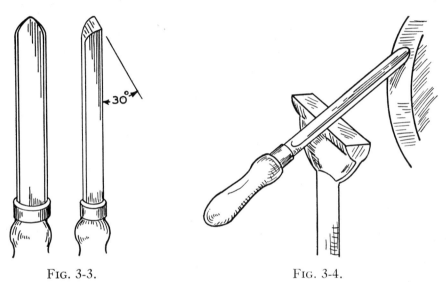

FIG. 3-3.   FIG. 3-4.

good grade of oilstone (q, Fig. 3-2) should be purchased for use in sharpening all of the tools. An India combination (coarse and fine) oilstone 8″ × 2″ × 1″ will be found suitable. A wood-turner's gauge shown as (r) in Fig. 3-2 is handy when turning cylinders.

The Care of the Tools. It is extremely important that all cutting tools be kept sharp. Sharp tools will produce smoother surfaces on the stock and make the shaping process much easier. All cutting tools must be ground and whetted from time to time as the work progresses. The length of time that a cutting tool can be used without sharpening will depend upon the kind of wood being turned and the care the worker gives the tool. It is not necessary to grind the cutting tool each time it becomes slightly dull. Whetting on an oilstone or with a slipstone will suffice unless the tool becomes nicked or extremely dull. The grinding and whetting operations are practically the same for each tool.

Grinding the Turning Tools. Tools may be ground on a high-speed electric grinder, on a hand-turned tool grinder, or a slow-speed wet-grinder. If the high-speed electric grinder is used, extreme care must be taken to prevent the tool from burning. The tool must be held lightly on the grinding wheel and also dipped *frequently* in water. During the grinding process the operator should always wear safety goggles to prevent getting particles of the grinding wheel in the eyes.

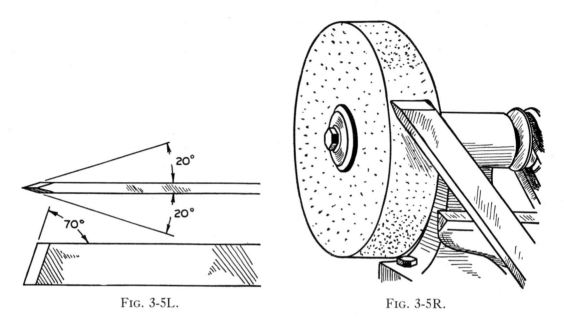

FIG. 3-5L.   FIG. 3-5R.

A. The *gouge* is ground so that the bevel has an angle of approximately 30°, Fig. 3-3. Place the gouge blade on the tool rest (Fig. 3-4) with the bevel down. Raise the handle slowly until the full length of the bevel is in contact with the wheel. Hold the tool lightly and roll it across the face of the wheel by turning

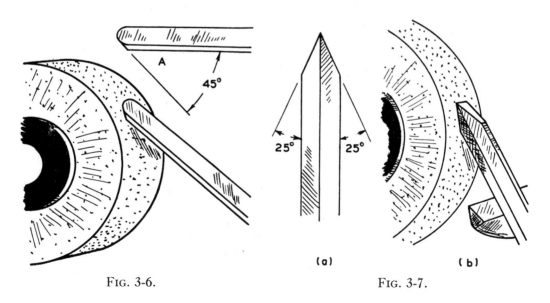

FIG. 3-6.   FIG. 3-7.

the handle slowly in a clockwise direction. Rotate the handle in the opposite direction and continue this process until the gouge is sharp.

B. The *skew* chisel is ground so that the cutting edge has an angle of 70° and the surfaces of the bevels are slightly rounded similar to the sides of an ax,

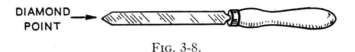

Fig. 3-8.

Fig. 3-5. Place the blade of the skew on the tool rest of the grinder and raise the handle slightly until the heel of the bevel comes in contact with the face of the wheel. Move the handle slightly to the right or left until the *cutting edge is parallel to the face of the wheel.* Now move the skew slowly and lightly, back and forth across the face of the wheel; at the same time raise the handle and lower it rapidly to produce the *slightly* rounded contour.

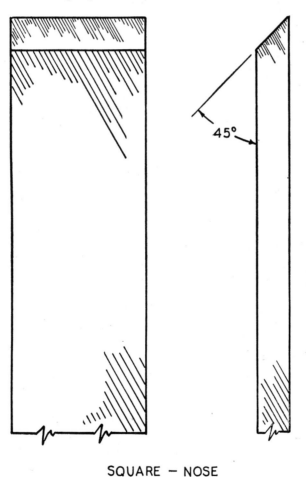

SQUARE — NOSE
TOOL

Fig. 3-9.

Turn the tool over and repeat the process on the opposite bevel. These operations are repeated until both bevels are equal and the edge is sharp.

C. The *round-nose* tool is ground with a bevel having an angle of approximately 45°, Fig. 3-6. Place the blade on the tool rest with the bevel down and

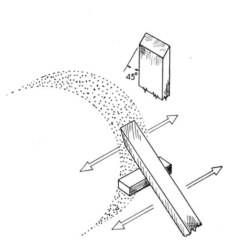

FIG. 3-10.

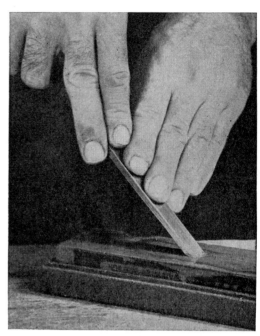

FIG. 3-11   Whetting a square-nose chisel.

FIG. 3-12   Whetting a square-nose chisel.

raise the handle slightly until the surface of the bevel comes in contact with the face of the wheel. Swing the handle in an arc from left to right and back again until a sharp edge is obtained.

    D. The *parting tool* is ground as shown in Fig. 3-7.

    E. The *diamond-point* tool is ground as shown in Fig. 3-8.

    F. The *square-nose* chisel is ground as shown in Fig. 3-9.

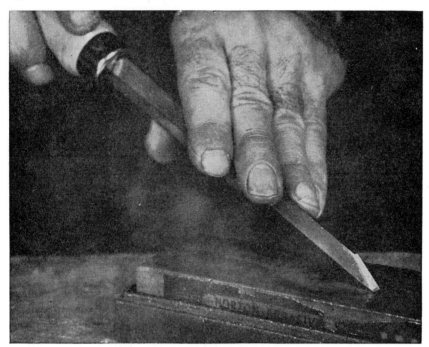

FIG. 3-13   Whetting a parting tool.

    All three of the above tools are ground by placing the blade on the tool rest with the bevel down (Fig. 3-10). Raise the handle slowly until the bevel comes in contact with the face of the wheel. Move the tool lightly back and forth across the face of the wheel until the edge is sharp.

Whetting the Turning Tools. The basic operation for the whetting of all of the turning tools is the same. The oilstone is fastened securely on a bench. Turn the coarse side of the oilstone up and squirt a few drops of oil on the surface. Place the bevel of the tool flat on the stone and move the tool in a circular motion from one end of the oilstone to the

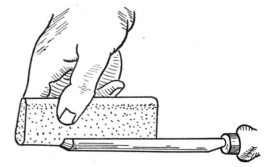

FIG. 3-14   Removing the wire-edge with a slipstone.

other (Fig. 3-11). Do not concentrate the whetting process on a small area of the stone as this will cause uneven wearing of the stone. The round-nose tool and the

FIG. 3-15   Holder for turning tools.

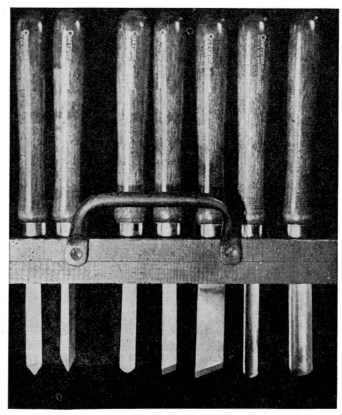

FIG. 3-16   Holder for turning tools.

gouge must be rolled from side to side while using the circular motion on the oilstone, so that all parts of the cutting edge may be whetted equally.

This part of the whetting operation will cause a wire-edge to be formed on the surface opposite to the bevel. On the flat tools, such as the square-nose chisel and the round-nose tool, the wire-edge is removed by turning the tool over so that the bevel is up. Lay the blade *flat* on the stone and continue the circular motion until the wire-edge is removed (Fig. 3-12).

Because the skew chisel and the parting tool have two bevels, the whetting must be done first on one bevel and then on the other (Fig. 3-13). The wire-edge is removed from a gouge by placing a few drops of oil in the inside curve of the blade. Then place the rounded edge of a slipstone firmly against the rounded inside portion of the blade and move it back and forth until the wire-edge is removed (Fig. 3-14). Care

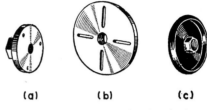

(a)   (b)   (c)

Fig. 3-17 (a) Small-sized face plate. (b) Large-sized face plate. (c) Hand-wheel.

must be taken to prevent forming a bevel on the flat surface.

On each tool the whetting process is continued, using the fine surface of the oilstone until the wire-edge is entirely removed and the cutting edge of the tool is sharp.

The turning tools should be kept in a holder that keeps them in easy reach of the operator and protects the cutting edges. Such a holder may be constructed by the home workshop owner (Figs. 3-15, 3-16).

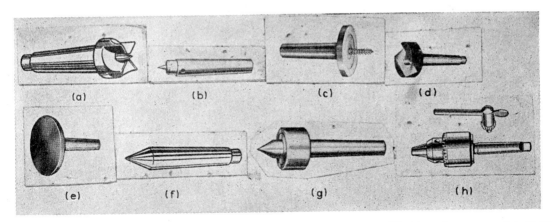

(a)   (b)   (c)   (d)

(e)   (f)   (g)   (h)

Fig. 3-18 (a) Spur center. (b) Cup center. (c) Screw center. (d) Crotch center. (e) Drill pad. (f) 60° plain center. (g) Ball bearing tailstock center. (h) Drill chuck.

Lathe Accessories. Most lathe manufacturers furnish various accessories for performing special operations or for making the basic operations easier to perform. The following group of accessories are common to most lathes and may be added to the lathe owner's equipment as needed.

Face plates of various sizes may be purchased. Fig. 3-17(a) illustrates a 3" face plate for small and medium face plate work. Fig. 3-17(b) illustrates a larger-sized face plate that may be used for outboard work. These are furnished in various sizes for different makes of lathes. Some manufacturers furnish a hand wheel to be fastened on the outside end of the live spindle, Fig. 3-17(c). Such a hand wheel is useful for quick stopping of the lathe and for ease in positioning the work. On some lathes, the hand wheel may be used as a face plate for outboard turning.

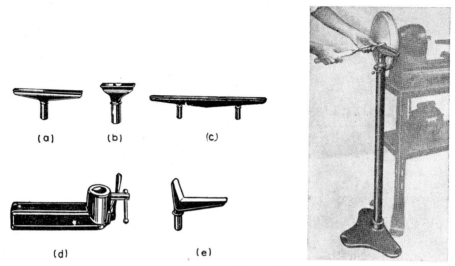

FIG. 3-19   (a) Standard tool rest.   (b) Short tool rest.   (c) Tool-rest with shanks.   (d) Tool-rest holder.   (e) Right-angle tool rest.   (f) Floor-stand tool rest holder.

Additional *centers* may be purchased for most lathes. It is well to have several spur centers, Fig. 3-18(a), and several cup centers, some having replaceable center points, Fig. 3-18(b). Another handy center is the screw center, Fig. 3-18(c), which is used for facing and hollowing operations on small pieces such as drawer knobs. The crotch center, Fig. 3-18(d), is useful when cross-drilling round stock. This center is inserted in the tailstock spindle. A drill pad shown in Fig. 3-18(e) is used in the tailstock spindle as a support when drilling flat or square work with a drill held in the headstock. The 60° plain center, Fig. 3-18(f), is used in the tailstock spindle when metal is being turned between centers. A ball bearing tailstock center, Fig. 3-18(g) is used for high-speed operations and for metal spinning on the wood-turning lathe. Fig. 3-18(h) illustrates a drill chuck which is usually inserted in the live spindle and is used for holding a drill or for holding small pieces of stock for turning. For lathes that do not have a hollow live spindle, drill chucks may be purchased that are threaded for mounting to the threaded end of the live spindle.

Tool rests are made in several sizes and styles. The standard tool rest, Fig. 3-19(a), is about 12" long. Shorter tool rests, about 4" long, are handy for small work, Fig. 3-19(b). A 24″ tool rest for extra-long turnings has two shanks, Fig. 3-19(c), and requires an extra tool-rest holder, Fig. 3-19(d). The right-angle tool rest is handy to use when doing inboard face-plate turning, Fig. 3-19(e). A rigid tool support is necessary when doing outboard face-plate turning. A floor-stand tool-rest holder may be obtained for this purpose, Fig. 3-19(f).

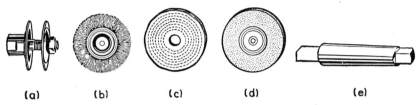

FIG. 3-20   (a) Screw-on arbor.   (b) Wire wheel.   (c) Buffing wheel.   (d) Grinding wheel.
(e) Tapered arbor for wheels.

Arbors may be obtained for holding various types of wheels. The screw-on arbor, Fig. 3-20(a), is used for holding wire wheels, Fig. 3-20(b), buffing wheels, Fig. 3-20(c), and grinding wheels, Fig. 3-20(d). A tapered arbor may be obtained which can be inserted in the hollow live spindle and which will accommodate many of the above-mentioned wheels, Fig. 3-20(e).

Sanding disks, Fig. 3-21, and *sanding drums*, Fig. 3-22, are handy accessories for the wood-turning lathe. These devices are time-savers for much of the work done in the home workshop. Disks and drums may be made by the worker if he

FIG. 3-21   FIG. 3-22   Sanding drum.   FIG. 3-23   Steady rest.
Sanding disk.

desires. Tables for supporting the work to be sanded may be made by the worker to be fastened to the ways of the bed of the lathe. Some manufacturers furnish such a table as an accessory.

A *steady rest*, Fig. 3-23, is handy to have when turning long, slender spindles. This device prevents the work from vibrating when the cutting tool is pushed into the stock. A satisfactory steady rest may be made of wood if the operator does not care to purchase one similar to that shown.

A special type of tool rest is necessary when doing metal spinning (see Fig. 5-23, page 57).

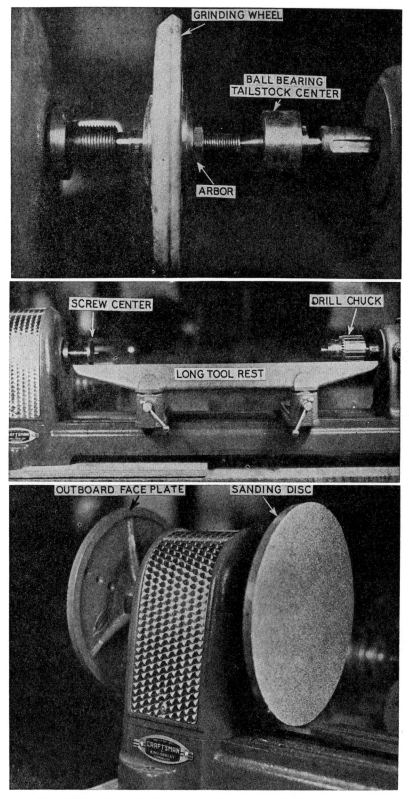

FIG. 3-24   Some lathe accessories mounted for operation.

IV

Basic Operations

Introduction. There are two generally accepted methods of turning: the scraping method and the cutting method. It is well for the beginner to acquire skill first in the scraping method. This method will be described first. After the beginning wood-turner has become skilled in the scraping method, he may then try the cutting method which is described in Section V. This method requires considerable more practice, but the results will be well worth the time spent.

§ I: SPINDLE TURNING (TURNING BETWEEN CENTERS)

A. Preparing the Stock and Setting Up the Work in the Lathe

1. Select and cut the stock to rectangular shape allowing approximately 1″ over the finished dimension in length and $\frac{1}{4}$″ over the largest finished diameter. The piece should be approximately square.

2. With a pencil and straightedge, draw lines diagonally across both ends of the stock. The point of intersection will be the approximate center.

3. If hardwood is used, make a saw kerf approximately $\frac{1}{8}$″ deep directly on the diagonal lines on one end of the stock. Use a backsaw to cut these lines. If softwood is used, this step is not necessary as the center can be driven into the wood without difficulty.

4. Remove the live, or spur, center from the headstock spindle with a knockout rod inserted through the hollow spindle. Hold the center with one hand to prevent it from falling on the lathe bed.

5. Place the piece of stock on end on a solid surface and with a heavy mallet drive the spur center into the end of the stock at the point of intersection of the lines, thus driving the spurs into the wood. If hardwood is used the spurs should be driven into the saw kerfs (Fig. 4-1).

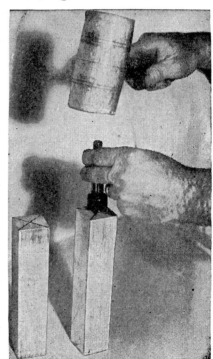

FIG. 4-1 Driving spur center into one end of stock in preparation for turning.

21

6. Insert the live center in the headstock spindle and, holding the stock in the left hand, move up the tailstock with the right hand until the point of the dead center is about $\frac{1}{4}''$ from the free end of the stock. Lock the tailstock in this position by tightening the tailstock clamp. Run the tailstock spindle out by turning the hand wheel on the tailstock and guide the point of the dead center into the end of the stock at the point of intersection of the lines until it is firmly embedded.

7. Turn the hand wheel back about a quarter turn and place several drops of oil on the point of the center where it enters the wood. Tighten the tailstock spindle clamp to prevent the vibration from loosening the stock.

Fig. 4-2   Square ready for turning.

8. Turn the stock by hand to see that it turns freely but without end play. If there is any end play, force the dead center a little farther into the end of the stock.

9. Move the tool-rest holder so that the tool rest is within $\frac{1}{8}''$ of the corners of the stock and parallel to it. Lock the tool-rest holder in this position. Set the top of the tool rest about $\frac{1}{16}''$ above the center of the piece of stock and lock it in this position. Revolve the stock once more, by hand, to see that no parts of the stock touch the tool rest. Fig. 4-2 shows the stock set up in the lathe ready for the first cut.

B. Turning to Size

It is suggested that the beginner spend a little time in practicing the various cuts before starting a project. He will then acquire the feel of the tools, learn how the tool performs, and acquire some accuracy in working to specific dimensions.

Such practice will prevent the waste of good materials and prevent the beginning wood turner from becoming discouraged if he makes an error. It is rather discouraging to spend considerable time turning a nice lamp, table leg, or bowl and then spoil the entire job when it is almost finished by pressing the tool a little too hard in the wrong place.

A series of exercises are described which involve the proper use of all the tools in the making of all types of cuts on the lathe. A knowledge of all these operations is necessary before starting an actual project as any turning will be a combination of any or all of these cuts.

I. *Turning a Cylinder.* (Fig. 4-3)

1. Obtain a piece of softwood such as white pine, basswood, or poplar 2″ thick, 2″ wide, and 9″ long.

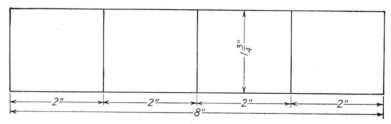

FIG. 4-3   Layout of cylinder.

2. Mount between centers as explained.

3. The first step in turning the cylinder is to rough off the corners of the wood with a gouge. Fig. 4-4 shows the correct position of the feet, body, and hands. The gouge is placed on the tool rest with the left hand firmly gripping the blade just back of the cutting edge. The right hand grips the end of the handle. The left wrist is dropped low enough so the heel of the palm rests on the tool rest to aid in guiding the gouge. The right hand is dropped slightly lower than the top of the tool rest and the arm is held against the body. The feet are spread about 12 to 15″ apart with the left side of the body closer to the lathe than the right side. Start the lathe on the medium speed for a piece this diameter. Roll the gouge slightly toward the tailstock and, beginning about 2″ from the end of the piece of wood nearest the tailstock, push the gouge straight into the stock until it begins to cut. Hold this position and slide the heel of the left palm along the tool rest toward the tailstock. This is repeated several times until most of the corners have been removed (Fig. 4-5).

4. Move the gouge several inches toward the headstock and repeat the process, removing the wood by sliding the gouge along the tool rest in the direction of the tailstock.

5. When the corners have been removed up to within several inches of the end of the stock nearest the headstock of the lathe, roll the gouge slightly toward

the headstock and then move the gouge in that direction, thereby removing the corners of the stock nearest the headstock of the lathe. As the corners are removed, the tool rest should be moved nearer the stock.

6. When all corners are removed and the piece of wood is round, the next step is to obtain the correct dimension. Set the calipers to $\frac{1}{8}''$ greater than the

FIG. 4-4   Proper position at the lathe.

FIG. 4-5   Reducing square stock to a cylinder.

finished dimension—in this case $1\frac{7}{8}''$, as shown in Fig. 4-6. Hold the parting tool in the right hand and the calipers in the left hand as shown in Fig. 4-7.

At intervals of approximately every $2''$, push the parting tool straight into the stock allowing the legs of the calipers to rest lightly in the groove being made.

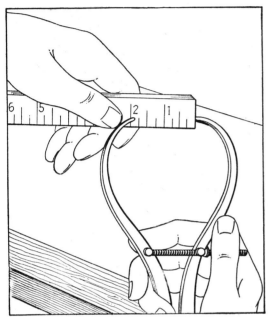

FIG. 4-6 Setting the calipers.

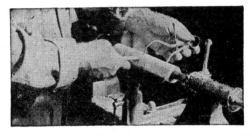

FIG. 4-7 Holding the parting tool and the caliper.

When the correct diameter is reached, the calipers will slide across the piece of stock.

7. The gouge is again used to remove the wood between the grooves made by the parting tool. This now leaves a cylinder approximately $\frac{1}{8}''$ larger than the finished diameter.

8. Now hold the skew chisel in the position shown in Fig. 4-8. The piece is

FIG. 4-8 Smoothing to a uniform diameter.

smoothed to exact size by lightly scraping off the remaining wood. Set the calipers to $1\frac{3}{4}''$, or the finished diameter of the piece and test by lightly touching the legs of the calipers to the cylinder in several places along its length. The legs of the calipers should just slip around the cylinder, without being forced.

II. Turning Shoulders.

1. On the cylinder just turned, hold the parting tool about $\frac{1}{2}''$ from the end of the stock nearest the tailstock of the lathe and make a groove. The bottom of

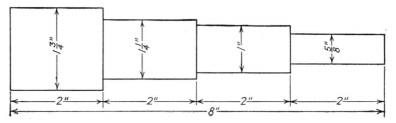

FIG. 4-9   Shoulder cuts.

the groove should be approximately $\frac{1}{2}''$ in diameter. This will produce a square end from which measurements can be taken with more accuracy.

2. Hold a rule on the top of the tool rest, measuring from the end just squared and, with the point of a pencil held at the 2'' mark, push the pencil lightly into the revolving stock (Fig. 4-10). Repeat this every 2'' so that the cylinder will be marked as shown in Fig. 4-9.

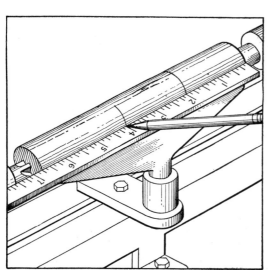

FIG. 4-10   Marking off with rule and pencil

3. Set the calipers at $\frac{3}{4}''$ and, with the parting tool, make a groove to this depth on the end of the cylinder nearest the tailstock. Make another groove the same depth next to the first line marked on the cylinder.

4. Change the setting of the calipers and cut grooves for each of the remaining sections of the cylinder. Outside of the last pencil mark, nearest the headstock of the lathe, cut a groove that will have a bottom approximately $\frac{1}{2}''$ in diameter.

5. With the gouge, remove the wood down to the bottom of each groove.

6. With the skew chisel, smooth each step on the cylinder. Check each diameter with the calipers set at the dimensions shown. Care must be taken when the point of the skew is brought up to each shoulder (Fig. 4-11).

Fig. 4-11   Smoothing to a shoulder with a skew.

III. *Turning Tapers.*

1. Mount a piece of stock 2″ thick, 2″ wide, and 9″ long between centers.
2. Turn to a cylinder $1\frac{5}{8}$″ in diameter.
3. Mark off the dimensions (Fig. 4-12) with a rule and pencil.

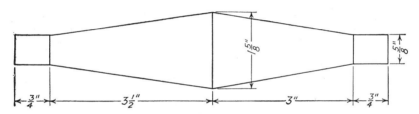

Fig. 4-12   Slim tapers.

4. With the parting tool, cut grooves to the diameter shown at the ends of the cylinder.

5. Starting at the ends, remove the wood with a gouge, working toward the ends to form the taper. The final cut should start almost at the line of the largest dimension and finish at the bottom of the groove.

6. Finish to required dimensions with the skew.

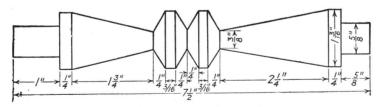

Fig. 4-13   Acute tapers.

IV. *Turning Acute Tapers and V-Cuts.*

1. Obtain a piece of stock $1\frac{3}{4}$″ thick, $1\frac{3}{4}$″ wide, and $8\frac{1}{2}$″ long. Mount between centers and turn to a $1\frac{3}{16}$″ diameter.

2. Lay out the dimensions according to Fig. 4-13.

3. Cut the shoulders on the ends of the stock.

4. Cut the V-groove by placing the skew chisel on the tool rest with the point down (Fig. 4-14). Push the point of the skew straight into the stock on the line

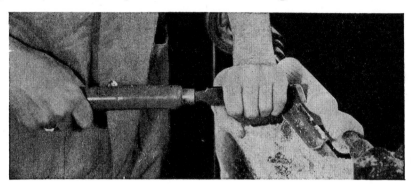

Fig. 4-14   Cutting a V-groove with a skew chisel.

marked for the center, or bottom, of the V-groove. Do not force too hard or the point of the skew will burn. In the same manner cut one side of the V to the correct width and depth, then work down the other side of the V.

5. Turn the tapers in the same manner as explained in the preceding section.

V. Concave Cuts.

1. Obtain a piece of stock 2″ square and 9″ long.

2. Turn to a cylinder having a diameter of $1\frac{3}{4}$″.

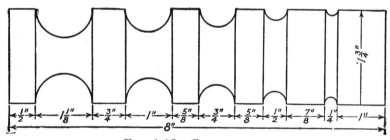

Fig. 4-15   Concave cuts.

Fig. 4-16   Turning a concave groove with a roundnose tool.

3. Lay out the marks for the grooves according to the dimensions shown in Fig. 4-15.

4. In the center of each prospective groove make a cut with the parting tool to the required depth, setting the calipers slightly over the finished dimension.

5. Place the roundnose tool flat on the tool rest, bevel down and push the tool straight into the stock (Fig. 4-16). Use the largest size tool available that will fit the groove being turned.

6. Concave cuts are tested for roundness by placing the outside corner of a

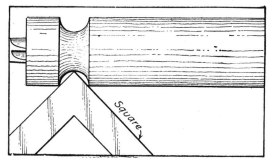

FIG. 4-17 Testing roundness of a concave groove.

square in the bottom of the groove with the sides of the square resting on the edges of the groove (Fig. 4-17).

VI. Turning Beads, or Convex Cuts.

1. Obtain a piece of stock $1\frac{3}{4}''$ square and $9''$ long.
2. Turn to a cylinder having a diameter of $1\frac{5}{8}''$.
3. Lay out beads according to the dimensions shown in Fig. 4-18.

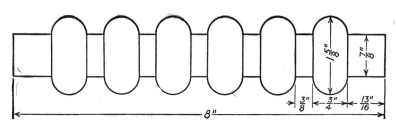

FIG. 4-18 Brads or convex cuts.

4. With the parting tool, cut to the required depth between each bead.
5. Mark off the center of each section which is to be a bead.
6. Lay the skew chisel flat on the tool rest, push the tool into the corner of a

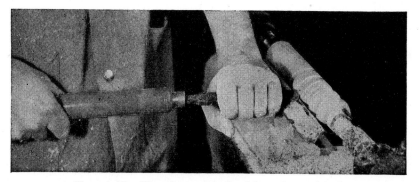

FIG. 4-19 Turning a bead with a skew chisel.

section which is to form the bead and move the handle of the skew slightly from side to side (Fig. 4-19) until one half the bead is rounded from the center of the bead to the bottom of the bead. Turn one half of each bead on the entire length of stock, then proceed with the other half of each bead. Beads may also be turned by using a diamond point tool in the same manner as the skew chisel.

VII. Turning Combination Cuts.

As previously stated, most turnings are a combination of two or more of the above described cuts. Fig. 4-20 indicates several of these combinations and it is suggested that the woodcrafter try both turnings before proceeding with a real project.

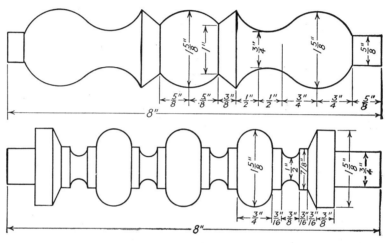

FIG. 4-20   Combination cuts.

VIII. Removing Waste Stock at the Ends of the Turning.

During the turning process, it will be noted that it is good procedure to start with a piece of stock slightly longer than that required for the finished dimensions. After the turning is completed and thoroughly sanded, the waste stock is cut off with a hand saw. Remove the turning from the lathe and clamp the waste end in a woodworker's vise. Use a backsaw and carefully saw the excess stock, holding the finished turning securely in one hand.

Another recommended method is to hold a backsaw pressed against the edge of a workbench as shown in Fig. 4-21. Holding the turning in both hands, move it back and forth over the teeth of the saw while revolving the piece slowly in the hands.

IX. Turning Objects with Rectangular Sections Remaining.

Many turnings require that sections be left in square or rectangular shape rather than being turned to a cylindrical shape. An example of this may be a turned table leg such as that shown in Fig. 4-22.

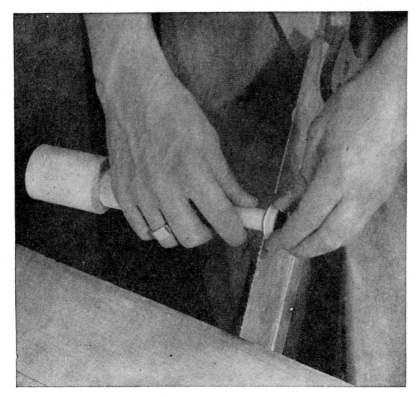

FIG. 4-21   Removing excess stock at ends of turning.

1. Lay out the rectangular piece of stock mounted between the centers of the lathe.

2. On the side of the line toward the section to be rounded, make a small nick with the long point of the skew chisel held in the same position as that for starting a V-groove. This will sever the wood fibers and prevent the rectangular corners of the turning from chipping.

3. Push the parting tool into the newly made nicks until the correct diameter is reached. This will leave the corners square and sharp—often desirable on some turnings.

4. Many turnings require that the sharp corners be rounded off. This is done by holding the skew with the long point down on the tool rest. Starting the

FIG. 4-22   A turning with rectangular sections.

point into the wood about $\frac{1}{8}''$ back from the square corners push the skew slowly into the stock at a slight angle. Gradually swing the handle of the chisel around to a position at right angles to the stock while pushing it into the wood to the required depth of the cut (Fig. 4-23).

Fig. 4-23   Rounding the corners of a square section.

§ II: Face-Plate Turning

Face-plate turning is performed by fastening a block of wood to a metal face plate, usually with screws. The face plate is threaded so that it can be screwed onto the live spindle of the lathe. The live center must first be removed from the spindle before attempting to screw on the face plate.

Generally, face-plate turning is done at slower speeds than spindle turning. For pieces over 8 inches in diameter, turn at the slowest speed.

A. Fastening Stock to a Metal Face Plate

1. One surface of the stock must be true and smooth. This is done by planing with a hand plane.

2. Draw diagonals from corner to corner locating the approximate center on the smooth face.

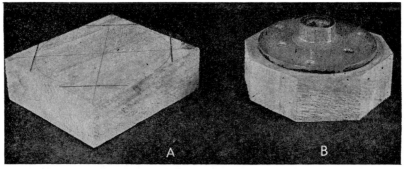

Fig. 4-24   (A) Stock lay-out for mounting on face plate.   (B) Stock mounted on face plate.

3. Set the dividers to the radius of the finished piece, plus $\frac{1}{8}''$ for truing up. From the approximate center of the piece of stock, scribe a circle with the dividers.

4. Draw tangents to the circle across each of the four corners (Fig. 4-24A). With a backsaw or a crosscut saw remove the waste wood to the tangent lines.

5. Select a face plate of the correct size (usually slightly smaller than the

finished diameter of the piece of stock, if available) and set the dividers at one half the diameter of the face plate, plus $\frac{1}{32}''$.

6. Using the same center, scribe a circle on the smooth face of the stock.

7. Place the face plate within this circle and center it so that no two screw holes will be directly in line with the grain of the wood.

8. Hold the face plate in position and mark the location of the screw holes on the wood by inserting a pencil or sharp-pointed tool in the screw holes. If the piece of stock is less than 6″ in diameter, three or four screws will be sufficient, depending on the number of screw holes in the face plate.

9. Remove the face plate and, with a small drill and drillstock, drill holes for the screws. The length and diameter of the screws used will be determined by the size of the stock being turned and also by the design. Screws must not be so long that the turning tool will hit them while the stock is being reduced. The worker will have to exercise some judgment regarding the size screws to use and therefore the size drill needed for the screw hole.

10. Replace the face plate in its original position and insert flathead screws into the holes. Tighten the screws securely with a screw driver (Fig. 4-24B).

B. Mounting Face Plate and Adjusting the Lathe

1. With a knock-out rod inserted in the hollow live spindle, remove the live center.

2. Wipe the threads on the live spindle with a piece of clean rag or cotton waste to remove any dirt.

3. Wipe the threads in the face plate.

4. Place a few drops of oil on the spindle threads and proceed to turn the face plate onto the spindle. Hold the pulley in one hand and tighten the face plate with the other hand.

5. Set the tool rest about $\frac{1}{8}''$ away from the stock and parallel to the bed of the lathe. Adjust the height of the tool rest so that its top is about $\frac{1}{8}''$ below the center of the spindle. Revolve the work by hand to make sure it will not hit the tool rest.

C. Truing Up the Stock

It is suggested that several practice pieces be turned before beginning a face-plate project. The exercises described here (Fig. 4-25 and Fig. 4-26) will provide practice in setting up the lathe and in using the tools necessary for face-plate turning.

1. Obtain a piece of softwood $1\frac{3}{4}''$ thick and $6\frac{1}{2}''$ square.

2. Plane one surface smooth and mount on the face plate as described in the preceding section.

3. Mount the face plate on the lathe and adjust the tool rest as described in preceding section.

4. Start the lathe in slow speed and, with the roundnose tool resting flat on the tool rest, bevel down, push the tool into the edge of the stock. There will be a tendency for the tool to jump because of the pointed edges of the wood. Grasp

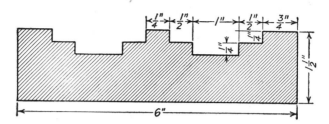

Fig. 4-25   Face plate turning of shoulders.

the blade securely in the left hand and with the heel of the palm resting against the front of the tool rest the tool can be guided carefully into the work. Keeping the tool at right angles to the work, slide the tool back and forth on the top of the tool rest, taking a light cut each time until the stock has been reduced to the required diameter (Fig. 4-27).

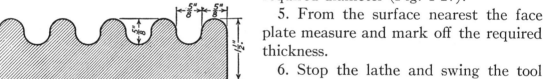

Fig. 4-26   Face plate turning of beads.

5. From the surface nearest the face plate measure and mark off the required thickness.

6. Stop the lathe and swing the tool rest around to the front of the stock and parallel to it about $\frac{1}{8}''$ away.

7. The lathe may be run at the next higher speed now that the stock is balanced and running true. Starting at the center of the piece of stock and with the roundnose tool held as shown in Fig. 4-28, remove the waste stock on the face of the piece. Start each cut at the center and work toward the outer edge.

Fig. 4-27   Reducing stock to diameter with roundnose tool.

FIG. 4-28   Facing stock to thickness with squarenosed tool.

8. When the waste stock has been removed almost to the line, smooth the surface by using either a squarenosed tool or a skew chisel in the same manner.

9. Stop the lathe and check the surface for smoothness and the edge for squareness as shown in Fig. 4-29.

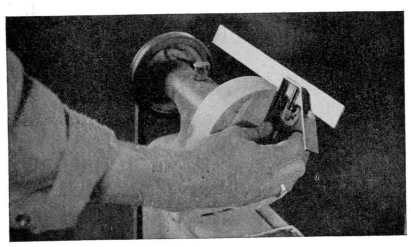

FIG. 4-29   Checking to squareness.

D. Shaping

1. On the surface of the trued piece of stock, mark off the lines according to the dimensions shown in Fig. 4-25.

2. With the parting tool cut to the required depth along each line, on the waste wood side.

3. Remove the wood with a roundnose tool or a squarenose tool. In either case the bottom of the recesses must be trued up smooth and square. This can be done with either a squarenose tool or, in the larger recesses, a skew chisel.

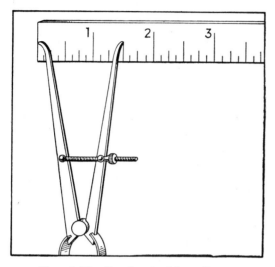

FIG. 4-30 Setting inside calipers.

4. The diameter of the recesses, or holes, is checked by use of inside calipers. The calipers are set as shown in Fig. 4-30. In using inside calipers the lathe must be stopped and the testing done as shown in Fig. 4-31. Correct depth is checked with a rule or a scale.

5. The procedure is exactly the same for turning the exercise piece shown in Fig. 4-26, except that the recesses are made with a roundnose tool and the beads are smoothed up with the skew chisel in the same manner that beads were made in spindle turning.

Grooves and beads can be made on the outside diameter of the stock in face plate turning in the same manner as. they are made in spindle turning, using the parting tool, roundnose tool and skew chisel.

FIG. 4-31 Checking diameter of a hole with inside calipers.

§ III: SANDING

Sanding should not be done until all turning is completed because particles of the flint or garnet from the sandpaper would become embedded in the wood and dull the tools. However, the sanding is done before the excess wood at the ends of the turnings has been cut off thereby losing the centers of the stock.

For most sanding, sizes $\frac{1}{2}$, 0, and 2/0 sandpaper are sufficient. Too coarse sandpaper will leave scratches on the wood and too fine sandpaper will not remove the irregularities fast enough.

The lathe should be run at about medium speed as too high a speed will cause the wood to burn under the sandpaper. In all sanding, the sandpaper must be moved back and forth toward the ends of the turning. If it is held in one place scratches will appear on the wood.

A. Sandpapering Straight Cylindrical Surfaces

1. Obtain a $\frac{1}{4}$ sheet of sandpaper and fold it several times so that a strip about $1\frac{1}{2}''$ wide will come in contact with the surface of the wood.

2. Start the lathe in medium speed and hold the sandpaper against the revolving work as shown in Fig. 4-32. Keep the sandpaper moving back and forth.

FIG. 4-32   Sanding a cylindrical surface.

3. Stop the lathe and refold the sandpaper to a convenient size and sand with the grain. This will remove any scratches left in sandpapering the revolving work.

B. Sandpapering Concave Grooves

1. Tear off a narrow strip of sandpaper and fold it between the fingers to a shape that corresponds to the shape of the groove.

Start the lathe and hold the sandpaper lightly against the revolving stock rolling it back and forth in the groove (Fig. 4-33).

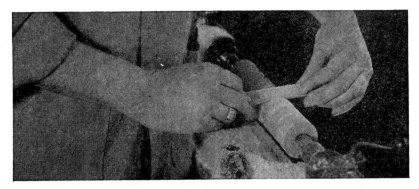

FIG. 4-33   Sanding a concave groove.

C. Sandpapering Beads and Shoulders

1. Fold a narrow strip of sandpaper and hold it between the thumb and forefinger of each hand.

2. Hold the sandpaper carefully against one side of the revolving bead and roll it up to the top of the bead. Sand the other side of the bead in the same

Fig. 4-34   Sanding a bead.

manner (Fig. 4-34). Care must be taken to prevent the bead from becoming flat and also care must be taken to prevent cutting into adjoining surfaces.

3. When sanding shoulders hold the strip of sandpaper in the same manner but be sure the sandpaper rests flat on the shoulder, then draw it gently back and forth.

§ IV: Applying Finish on the Lathe

The most common type of finish performed on a lathe is a shellac-oil finish and polish which is often called "French polishing."

1. After the turning has been completely sanded the lathe is stopped and the work is thoroughly dusted.

2. Place a piece of paper on the bed of the lathe, under the turned stock, to prevent the finishing materials from dripping on the lathe.

3. Without having the lathe revolving, apply a thin coat of shellac to the work with a brush.

4. Allow to dry for several hours and sand lightly with 4/0 sandpaper, while the work revolves at medium speed. Care must be taken not to cut through the shellac. Stop the lathe and dust the work thoroughly.

5. Obtain a piece of soft clean cloth, such as cheesecloth, and fold it four or five times to form a pad about 4″ square.

6. Lift up the last fold and moisten the center of the pad with fairly thin shellac (approximately 3 parts shellac and 1 part alcohol). Replace the top fold of the pad and apply a few drops of linseed oil.

7. Start the lathe at medium speed and hold the pad against the revolving

work (Fig. 4-35). Move the pad back and forth from end to end of the turning being sure to touch all places. A medium and uniform pressure is maintained. Too much pressure is apt to lift the shellac from the wood, or cause it to pile up.

8. Allow the shellac to dry thoroughly and apply at least five or six coats in the manner described.

If the shellac is too thick it will pile up and form streaks on the turning. When this occurs, apply a few more drops of linseed oil to the pad and apply a little extra pressure on the piled-up shellac. The pressure will cause the shellac to heat up and it should then flow smoothly on the work. If this procedure does not remove the piled-up shellac, moisten a clean rag with alcohol and apply to the revolving work. The alcohol will remove the shellac and necessitate a new application.

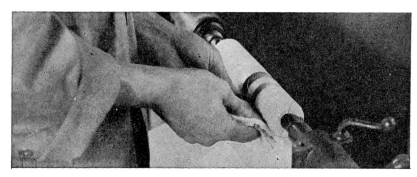

FIG. 4-35   Applying a French polish.

If too much oil and not enough shellac has been applied the woodcrafter can rub the finish entirely off the work with his finger. French polishing gives a beautiful finish to turned projects but it is not too durable.

9. It may be desired to stain the wood before applying a French polish. After the turning has been thoroughly sanded and dusted, apply a water or oil stain in the usual manner. Allow to dry from 12 to 24 hours and sand very lightly, dust, and proceed with the French polish. If an open-grain wood such as walnut, mahogany, or oak is used, a paste filler should be applied between the staining and French polishing operation. After applying either stain or filler it is best not to start the work turning until the stain or filler is thoroughly dry as the finish may have a tendency to be driven out of the wood rather than to penetrate into the pores.

§ V: Cutting Method of Turning

The gouge and the skew chisel are the two turning tools most frequently used in the cutting method. Other turning tools are used as scraping tools. The work is mounted in the lathe, between centers, as described for the scraping method. The gouge is held for turning cylindrical work as follows:

The gouge is placed on its edge on the tool rest. The left hand is used to hold the blade firmly on the tool rest. Hold the end of the handle in the right hand and lower the hand slightly. Bring the gouge carefully into contact with the revolving stock and move the gouge along the tool rest taking a shearing cut (Fig. 4-36).

The gouge is used for making concave cuts by the cutting method as follows:

Fig. 4-36.

Fig. 4-37.

Place the gouge on the tool rest, on its edge, and move it slowly into the turning stock. At the same time the gouge is pushed forward, it is rolled over, keeping the bevel of the gouge against the surface which has just been cut (Fig. 4-37). This controls the amount of cut. The cut is made only to the center of the groove. Turn the gouge over and repeat the operation for the other half of the groove.

After work has been turned to a cylinder with the gouge, it may be smoothed with the skew chisel as follows:

Start the lathe and place the skew chisel flat on the revolving cylinder and touching the tool rest at about the center of the tool rest. Draw the chisel slowly backward until the heel of the bevel comes into contact with the work. Swing

Fig. 4-38.

the handle of the chisel in the opposite direction to which the cut is to be made and slightly upward until the center of the cutting edge comes in contact with the work. With the chisel held in this position, move it steadily forward taking a light cut (Fig. 4-38). Be sure to keep the chisel firmly on the tool rest. At the end of the cut, turn the chisel over and, starting in the middle of the work, make a similar cut in the opposite direction.

Beads may be cut with a skew chisel in the following manner:

Start the lathe and then place the back of the skew chisel on the tool rest. Push the point of the skew into the work at the outside edge of the bead making a V-groove (Fig. 4-39). Lay the skew chisel flat on the tool rest and on the revolving piece at the center of the top of the bead. Draw the chisel back slowly, bringing the heel of the bevel into contact with the work. Roll the chisel slowly over in the direction which the cut is to follow. With the heel of the bevel take a light cut (Fig. 4-40). Be sure to keep the bevel of the chisel tangent with the surface of the bead and let the heel of the chisel do the cutting. As the cut is being made, raise the handle of the chisel slowly and at the same time swing the handle

Fig. 4-39.

Fig. 4-40.

Fig. 4-41.

toward the right or the left, depending on which side of the bead is being cut (Fig. 4-41). Cut the other half of the bead from the center of the top of the bead.

§ VI: Outboard Face Plate Turning

Circular pieces which are too large to turn on a face plate over the bed of the lathe may be turned on a face plate mounted on the outside end of the spindle. The stock is mounted on a face plate in the same manner as for work done over the lathe bed. Extreme care must be taken to fasten the work securely to the face plate, using a sufficient number of screws of a size that will give the maximum holding power. The size of the pieces which may be turned will be determined by the size of the lathe. Work over 20″ in diameter should not be attempted on the small bench lathes since the vibration caused by the revolving work may be greater than the lathe can stand.

When the work is mounted on the lathe, the floor-type tool rest is set up in the same manner as the regular tool rest (Fig. 4-42). Be sure and revolve the work by hand to make certain that there is sufficient clearance between the work and the tool rest. *The work must be revolved at the slowest spindle speed while doing outboard turning.*

Proceed to turn the stock in the same manner as is done when turning on the face plate over the lathe bed. Use only the scraping method.

§ VII: Fluting and Reeding

Flutes and reeds are often used to enhance the appearance of many kinds of turnings. Although these decorations cannot be made while the lathe is turning, the lathe is used as a holding device for the work. After the stock has been turned to the desired dimensions and contours, the work is left mounted on the lathe.

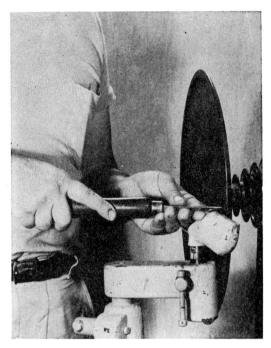

FIG. 4-42.

If the lathe is equipped with an index head, or dividing head, the layout of the flutes or reeds is greatly simplified. The locking pin is pressed into one of the holes on the dividing head. This holds the work in position while the flutes or reeds are cut by hand with gouges or chisels. If a portable electric router is available, the flutes or reeds may be cut with suitable shaper cutters.

After cutting the first flute or reed, the locking pin is pulled out of the hole in the index head. The work is revolved by hand to the next pre-determined hole in the index head and the work is again locked in position. The use of this device insures a reasonable amount of accuracy in dividing the circumference of the work into any number of equal parts, as well as to hold the work securely while the decorative cuts are being made.

Be sure that the pin is removed from the index head before switching on the motor for turning operations.

§ VIII: TEMPLATES

A turning template is a measuring instrument made by the craftsman. It is usually a full-sized pattern of the desired contour of a turned piece. The template, or pattern, may be made from thin wood, sheet metal, or cardboard. The template is a valuable measuring tool to use when making duplicate parts or where identical turnings are desired. The contours of most turnings are irregular in shape and the outline of the desired finished turnings can be laid out on the template material with rule, French curve, and compass. The template should be carefully cut to shape as any errors in this measuring instrument will be duplicated in all turned objects. If thin wood is used for the template, the edge of the outline should be beveled. This will make it easier to determine when the contour of the turning matches the contour of the template. Sheet metal is generally used for templates when a large quantity of duplicate turnings are to be made. For all practical purposes, cardboard is the ideal material for templates as it is easily cut. To use the template, place it upon the work being turned. When the turning matches the template and no light comes between the two, the turning is complete. See Project 30 for use of templates.

V

Advanced and Special Operations

§ I: Turning Keene's Cement

Many articles designed for wood-turning can also be turned from Keene's cement if the craftsman so desires. Such projects as table lamps, bowls, powder boxes, ash trays, book ends, decorative spiral columns, plates and vases can be made in solid colors, imitation marble effects, or left in the natural white color of the cement.

Keene's cement is manufactured from gypsum which is calcined (burned) at a red heat (1500° F). It is then treated in an alum bath and, after drying, is again burned. The cement is subsequently ground to a fine powder similar to plaster. The cement, when mixed with water, dries very slowly to a hard substance. The cement is considerably harder and stronger than ordinary plaster.

It may be purchased in 100-pound bags and the cost is only a few cents per pound. The cement may be colored with Lime-Proof Plaster colors. These colors come in a dry powder and are usually sold by the pound. Both the cement and the colors can be purchased from practically any builder's supply firm.

Most craftsmen construct a cylindrical sheet metal mold to receive the liquid cement. (See Fig. 5-1.) The mold should be made slightly greater than the largest diameter of the article to be made and slightly longer than the longest dimension. It should be constructed to facilitate easy removal after the cement has set. Stove bolts are used to hold the mold together. A base should be turned to close one end of the sheet metal mold. A rebate, or step, is generally turned in the wooden base to provide a friction fit for the sheet metal cylinder. If the cement project, such as a bowl or ash tray, is to be made on a face plate, a wooden base similar to the one shown in Fig. 5-2 should be turned. This base may be made from a piece of $\frac{3}{4}''$ stock. Before fastening the wood to the face plate with wood-screws, drive four screws into the wood. These four screws should extend through the wood and well into the space formed by the sheet metal mold. The purpose of these four screws is to fasten or hold the block of cement to the wooden base after the liquid cement has set and the mold has been removed. The face plate, holding both the master-base and block of soft cement, is then mounted on the headstock of the lathe for turning. (See Figs. 5-2 and 5-3.)

Between-Center Turning. If the cement project, such as a table lamp, is to be turned between centers, a wood base similar to the one shown in Fig. 5-4 should

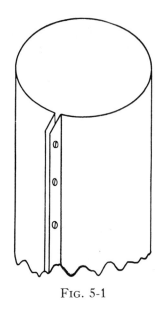

FIG. 5-1

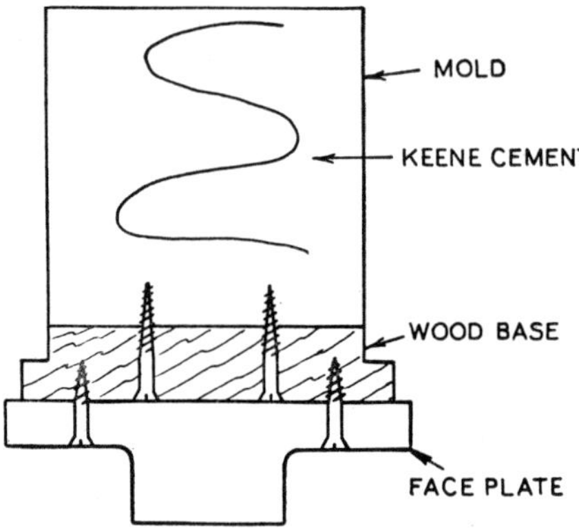

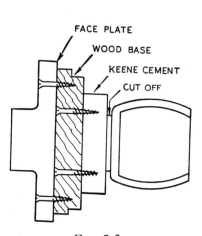

FIG. 5-2

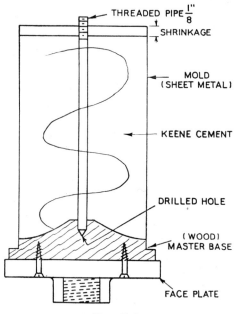

FIG. 5-3.

FIG. 5-4.

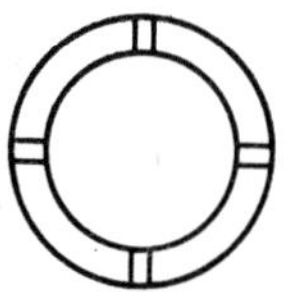

FIG. 5-5.

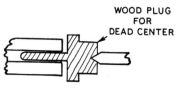

FIG. 5-6.

be made. The base should be turned from a piece of 2″ stock. In addition to the rebate for the cylindrical sheet metal mold, note the tapered shape of the surface of the base. This provides a concave shape in the bottom of the lamp. A $\frac{3}{8}$″ hole is drilled into the center of the base to hold a length of $\frac{1}{8}$″ pipe (the outside diameter of $\frac{1}{8}$″ pipe is approximately $\frac{3}{8}$″). The hole should not be drilled to a depth greater than one-half the height of the tapered section of the base. The reason for this is to prevent the pipe from extending beyond the bottom of the lamp and to provide room for concealed wiring. The pipe should be threaded at the upper end to receive a lamp socket. Continuous threaded brass pipe is the best to use as it will not rust. The upper end of the pipe is plugged with clay or by dropping a wood screw in the open end to prevent the liquid cement from filling the pipe when the mold is poured. When the cement has set, the mold is removed and the block of cement is removed from the wooden base. A lathe drill chuck is fastened to one end of the pipe and inserted into the hollow spindle of the head stock. If a lathe drill chuck is not available one end of the pipe can be notched with a hack saw (Fig. 5-5) to receive the spurs of a live center. The other end of the pipe is held by a 60° tailstock center. Be sure to grease this end of the pipe to reduce friction while turning. If the article, such as a pedestal, is to be turned between centers, holes may be drilled in the center of each end of the cement block and wooden plugs inserted (Fig. 5-6) to receive the lathe centers.

Mixing the Cement. Keene's cement for lathe projects may be mixed in a bowl or some other type of container and stirred with a large mixing spoon or wooden paddle. Usually two parts of cement are mixed with one part of water by volume. Extra water or cement should be added to obtain the consistency of thick cream. After the batch has been thoroughly stirred, the bowl should be jounced against the surface of a table or bench to cause any air bubbles to rise to the surface and break. The thinner the mixture, the easier it is to remove the air bubbles in the solution.

If the craftsman desires a solid-colored article, the dry powdered color should be stirred into the liquid cement before the batch is poured into the mold. If an imitation marble effect is desired, fill the mold only partially with the liquid cement. Use a pinch of dry powdered color, only enough to cover the tip of a screwdriver, and place it on the surface of the cement in the mold at three or four different points. "Cut" the color into this layer of the cement with the screwdriver. Six to ten strokes with the screwdriver are sufficient. This will give the article a marble effect. Repeat color applications with successive layers of cement until the mold is completely filled.

In drying or setting, the cement will shrink in proportion to the amount of water used. It usually shrinks or settles from $\frac{1}{4}$″ to $\frac{1}{2}$″ per foot. The cement should stand for 12 to 20 hours before turning.

Turning speeds should be as slow as possible, not over 600 rpm. The regular set of wood-turning tools are used. The soft cement will not turn or remove the temper from the steel. If the cement is allowed to dry too long, however, it may remove the keen edge of the tool. The keen edge can be replaced by proper whetting.

The craftsman can determine if the cement is in proper turning condition if the shaving comes off in a long ribbon, often reaching the floor without breaking. If the shaving comes off as a powder, the cement is too dry. If the shaving is weak and too soft, allow more drying time before turning.

To repair tears or air holes in the cement use waste shavings. These have the same moisture content as the project and will make a perfect patch. These air holes may be filled by pressing the damp shavings into the air holes with the thumb. When the article has been turned to dimension, set it aside to dry. It should dry at least 12 days before being polished. Clean and oil all lathe surfaces and accessories which have come into contact with the cement to prevent any rust.

The article must be remounted in the lathe for finishing. Sand the surface smooth with wet-dry sandpaper, dipping the paper frequently into water. The article can then be polished with a very fine abrasive called tripoli. Place some powdered tripoli on a cloth which has been slightly dampened and polish the article while it is turning in the lathe. Buff the article with a dry cloth. The friction will bring out the polish. After polishing, wax may be applied with a soft cloth. Keene's cement is porous; therefore, if the article is to contain water, it should be designed so that a glass container can be inserted.

§ II: Spiral Columns

Spiral columns made from wood have been used for several hundred years as a means of decorating furniture. Although the making of a spiral column is not strictly a turning procedure, it may be conveniently made on the lathe. The craftsman might find this process valuable in making such articles as spiral-

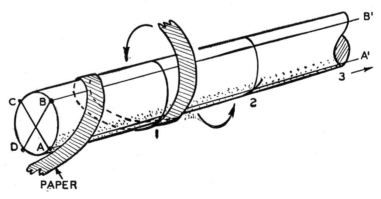

Fig. 5-7   Basic layout for uniformly turned wooden cylinder.

column lamp bases, pilasters made from a split turning to decorate cabinet fronts, or even structural members of various articles of furniture.

Basic Layout. The layout of practically all spiral turnings is basically the same and is made on the piece while it is mounted in the lathe. Figure 5-7 shows the basic layout of a uniformly turned wooden cylinder. The end of the cylinder shown in Fig. 5-7 shows the diagonal saw cuts which were made when the stock was centered for mounting in the lathe. These are indicated by the letters AC and DB. The tool rest is used as a straightedge upon which to rest a pencil. A pencil line is then drawn horizontally, from the ends of each saw cut, throughout the entire length of the piece. These lines are indicated by AA' and BB' and would be similarly drawn for C and D. This divides the cylinder into four equal quarters, lengthwise.

The craftsman should determine the number of turns in the spiral he wishes to have in the project before proceeding further with the layout. Often the spiral advances, in one revolution, a distance equal to the diameter of the stock. In any event, divide the length of the piece into the number of parts (turns) desired. The layout of the spiral in Fig. 5-7 is for two complete turns around the cylinder.

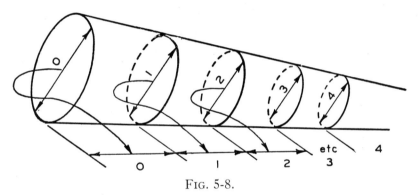

FIG. 5-8.

Start the lathe. Lay a rule on the tool rest. Mark the lengths of the turns by placing a pencil point on the revolving cylinder at the predetermined dimensions. These divisions are indicated at 1 and 2 in Fig. 5-7. A piece of heavy paper may be used as a straightedge on point A. Wrap the paper around the cylinder so that the same edge of the paper passes through point 1. Draw the first spiral guide line for the first turn. The above operations are repeated for each complete turn until a continuous spiral guide-line spirals around the entire cylinder.

Tapered Spiral Layout. The basic layout of the spiral guide lines on a tapered column differs from the foregoing operations in one respect. The length of the first division is equal to the diameter of the piece. (See O, Fig. 5-8.) The length of the next division is equal to the diameter of the tapered column at point 1. The length of the next division is equal to the diameter of the tapered column at 2. Each complete turn becomes smaller as the column decreases in diameter. The various diameters may be measured with the outside spring calipers.

Double Spiral Layout. The double spiral is by far the most popular type of twisted turning. It may be made on both straight and tapered cylinders. The basic layout of the cylinder is the same as for the single spiral. A single spiral guide line is laid out around the cylinder as previously described. Another spiral guide line is laid out from point C (Fig. 5-7) in the same direction as the one laid out from point A. When the spiral is formed it will have the familiar twisted rope effect.

Forming the Spiral. Using a back saw, cut along the spiral guide lines to a depth of $\frac{1}{2}''$ to $\frac{3}{4}''$. The larger the diameter of the column, the deeper the saw kerf. With a $\frac{1}{2}''$ wood chisel or a knife, cut on both sides of the saw kerf. This will give a large spiral V-cut. Shape the spiral with a wood rasp. Turn the lathe by hand and sand the column. The sandpaper should be moved along the spiral as the lathe turns. The craftsman should not forget to plan for extra wood at both ends of the spiral column for finishing the various turned designs or for appropriate joints.

It is possible to make concave spiral turnings in much the same manner as the convex spiral turnings are made. Spiral guide lines are laid out. The wood between the guide lines is removed with a knife or with the convex side of a wood rasp.

§ III: Split Turning

A split turning is generally one-half of a turned cylindrical column. It is used extensively by the pattern-maker to make split patterns for casting and by the cabinetmaker for decorating various kinds of furniture. Such projects as book ends, wall shelves, and similar half-round articles are popular.

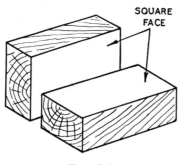

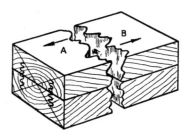

FIG. 5-9.   FIG. 5-10.

To make a split turning two pieces of wood (Fig. 5-9) are placed face to face and fastened together at the ends. This may be done with corrugated steel fasteners (see End A, Fig. 5-10) or with counterbored woodscrews. The two pieces may be glued together with non-absorbent heavy paper placed in the joint. The stock is centered, mounted, and turned in the lathe in the usual manner. Care should be taken not to hit the end fastenings with the lathe tools.

This requires stock in excess of the total length of the design (see Fig. 5-11). After the piece has been turned and finished in the lathe, the waste ends, containing the fasteners, are sawed off the turned piece (see C and D, Fig. 5-12). If glue and paper have been used to join the two pieces, they may be split apart by inserting

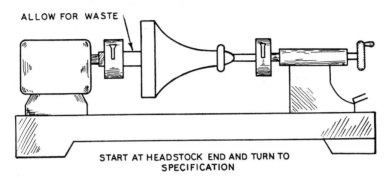

ALLOW FOR WASTE

START AT HEADSTOCK END AND TURN TO
SPECIFICATION

FIG. 5-11.

the cutting edge of a chisel into the end of the joint. The turned column will now fall into two half columns. Each half column will have a flat back (Fig. 5-13) and it can be applied flush to a wall, cabinet front, or other type of vertical or horizontal flat plane.

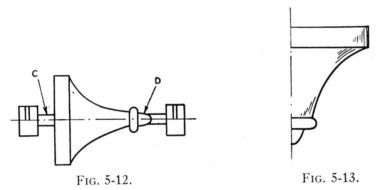

FIG. 5-12.   FIG. 5-13.

§ IV: FORM TOOLS FOR WOOD-TURNING

When enough pieces of any one shape are desired to warrant the making of a form tool, often production can be facilitated by use of this special item. The method used is to rough the stock down to cylindrical shape and then push the form tool into the work similar to the method used in laying out work with a parting tool.

The use of a form tool requires a lot of power to rotate the piece and, if the wood is a soft wood, sometimes the spur center will twist or spin if care is not used in the procedure. The form tool when taking a full cut on the wood will sometimes cause chatter or leave the work rough. It is a tool that you cannot, without practice, pick up and expect to do finished work. It must be eased into the work in such a manner that it will not chatter, will not spin the spur center, and will arrive at the desired size by overcoming the difficulties. These tools are generally made of a piece of flat tool steel on which the form is laid out and then ground to shape, with a handle attached, and hardened and tempered. Form tools usually are of a **scraping** type. Consequently, considerable sanding of the pieces must be done after **they** are used. If one must pay to have the tool made, it would be wise to check on costs before investing in this type of equipment.

§ V: Drilling

The wood lathe may be conveniently used to do various drilling jobs. In this process the spur center and the tailstock cup center are removed. A drill chuck

Fig. 5-14   Drill chuck.

mounted on the correct taper shank is inserted in the head-stock (Fig. 5-14). The drill is held in the chuck and the work piece may be forced into the turning drill by using the tailstock sleeve and screw. Various tailstock jigs may be utilized to provide a greater degree of support during the drilling process. A set of fractional-sized drills ranging in size from $\frac{1}{16}''$ to $\frac{1}{2}''$ by $\frac{1}{16}''$ is recommended. Probably a $\frac{1}{2}''$ size drill chuck will be the most practical size. This will allow the worker to utilize the chuck for turning small rods and to bore larger holes with machine shank Forstner bits.

§ VI: Oval Turning

Most all lathe turnings are cylindrical in shape. The cross-section views of these turnings are full-round or circular. It is possible, however, to make oval turnings in the lathe. The cross-section views of these turnings will be elliptical in shape (see shaded area in Fig. 5-15). A hammer or mallet handle is an example of this type of turning. Oval turnings are made by mounting the work piece in the

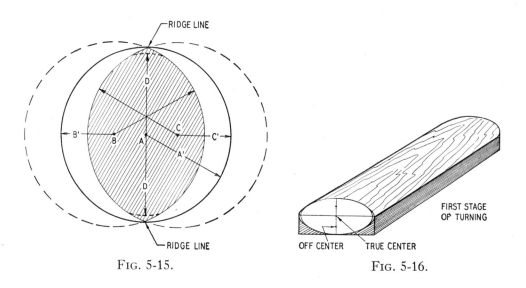

Fig. 5-15.   Fig. 5-16.

lathe on two points off the true center. The true center of the work piece is used only at the beginning and finish of the process.

Procedure (see Figs. 5-15 and 5-16):

1. Turn a cylinder to a diameter slightly larger than the major diameter of the desired elliptical turning (see radius A′, Fig. 5-15).

2. Remove the cylinder from the lathe and lay out the two points for mounting the stock for turning the minor diameter of the project. (See centers B and C, Fig. 5-15.)

3. Remount the work piece on one set of the above-mentioned points. (Say, B of Fig. 5-15.) Adjust lathe to slowest possible speed. Turn one half of elliptical turning. It will be noticed that the other part of the work piece (B′) will rotate beyond the reach of the turning tool. As the work revolves, two images are formed. Where the images appear to meet or merge is the ridge line of the work piece. It will be noticed (Fig. 5-15) that the ridge lines are at either end of the major diameter. Thus, cuts can be taken until they meet the ridge line.

4. Remount the work piece on off-center C and turn the other half of the elliptical turning.

5. After completing both sides of the elliptical turning, it will be noticed that both ridge lines will appear as rather sharp edges. Remount the work piece on true center A and trim off the sharp ridge line edges. (See D, Fig. 5-15.) Sanding will further refine the true elliptical form.

6. It is also possible to make a piece that is elliptical at one end and round at the other by off setting only one end of the work piece.

§ VII: CHUCK TURNING

Chuck turning is a more advanced operation for the wood turner to attempt and should not be endeavored until he has mastered the basic operations, both in spindle and also in face plate turning. The chuck is a device designed to hold pieces which cannot be conveniently held by ordinary methods. Chucks for wood-turning are usually made of wood. The wooden chuck block is generally fastened to the face plate and turned so that it may receive the work and hold it by friction while it is being turned.

For the most part, chuck turning requires the same tool operations as those used in face plate work, although lighter cuts are desirable since the work is not as securely held as in other methods of turning. A good example of chuck work may be found in the turning of a bowl. The hollow may be first turned and the outside finished as far as is practicable while the work is screwed to the face plate. The bowl is then removed from the face plate and reversed, holding it in a chuck while the bottom and foot are turned.

Although there is no standard design for a wooden chuck, certain guiding principles will enable the turner to design one which will most efficiently hold the work. In general there are two types of chucks. Probably the most common is the *outside chuck* (Fig. 5-17). An outside chuck is designed to grasp the work piece on the outside. This type chuck has a recess turned into its face into which the work piece is forced.

An inside chuck (Fig. 5-18) is used when the work to be turned has a hole or recess. In this type of chuck, the work is pressed over the chuck and thus held for subsequent turning operations.

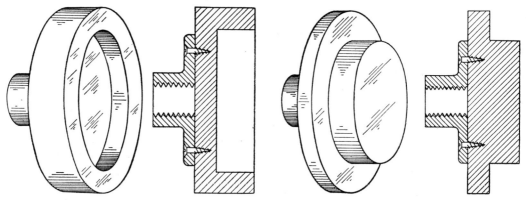

FIG. 5-17   Outside chuck.   FIG. 5-18   Inside chuck.

End grain of soft closed-grained woods are best for the construction of large chucks. If the face grain of the wood is used, the chuck may shrink unevenly soon after the recess is turned. Each chuck is made to fit a particular job. Large chucks can be made by fastening a set of four blocks to a block of wood on the face plate (Fig. 5-19). The blocks are placed so that, when turned, they will accommodate

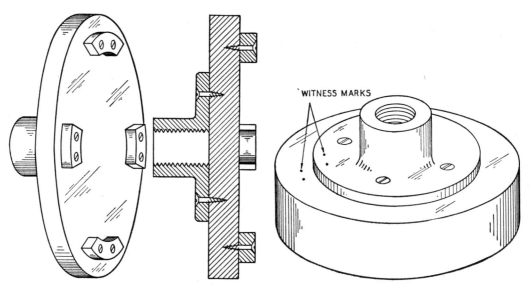

FIG. 5-19   Chucks made of blocks.   FIG. 5-20   Witness marks.

the work piece. This method may be used for either inside or outside chuck turning.

Although there may be no immediate subsequent use for the chuck blank after it has once been used, it may be stored and used again. If reuse of the chuck is anticipated, always mark the face plate and chuck with a "witness" mark (Fig. 5-20) so that the chuck may be easily relocated on the face plate in the original position.

§ VIII: TURNING A SPHERE

The turning of a sphere is an example of the use of an outside chuck. The preliminary work is done on the blank while it is being held between centers.

Procedure (see Fig. 5-21):

1. Select square stock about ½″ larger and about 1″ more in length than the finished spherical diameter.

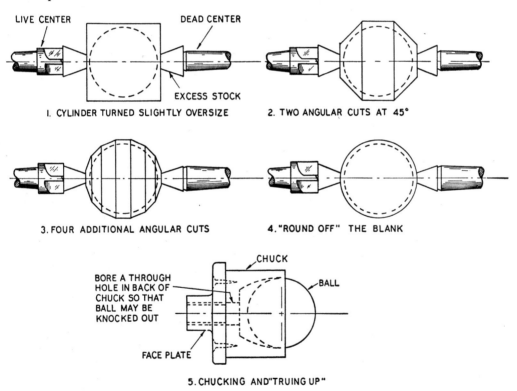

FIG. 5-21   Turning a sphere.

2. Prepare the stock for turning between centers and turn to a diameter approximately ⅛″ larger than the finished diameter.

3. Make two angular cuts at a 45° angle and tangent to an imaginary sphere which is ⅛″ oversize. A full-size layout of these cuts is desirable in order to determine how much to cut from the blank.

4. Four additional angular cuts are then taken. Each cut is made tangent to the imaginary-oversize sphere.

5. "Round off" the blank by cutting off the corners.

6. Remove the waste stock from the center ends.

7. Prepare an outside chuck to receive the spherical blank. The sphere should be held tightly by the chuck when slightly less than half of the sphere protrudes.

8. Force the blank into the chuck.

9. Take light cuts on the sphere to "true up" the shape. Rotate the blank one-quarter of a turn in the chuck and repeat the truing-up procedure until the sphere is completely trimmed. If the sphere becomes too small for the chuck, the size of the chuck may be reduced by turning a deeper depression in it.

10. Sand the sphere and finish as desired.

§ IX: Turning a Ring

Turning a circular ring is another common wood-turning job which requires chucking. Depending upon their shape and size, rings may be held by inside or outside chucks for the secondary turning operations. The ring herein described will be turned on an *inside chuck*.

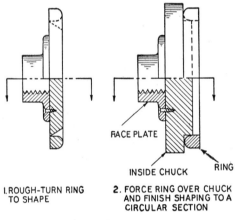

FACE PLATE

INSIDE CHUCK   RING

1. ROUGH-TURN RING TO SHAPE

2. FORCE RING OVER CHUCK AND FINISH SHAPING TO A CIRCULAR SECTION

FIG. 5-22 Turning a ring.

Procedure (see Fig. 5-22):

1. Select the stock for the ring about $\frac{1}{4}''$ thicker and $\frac{1}{2}''$ larger than the outside diameter of the required ring.

2. Fasten this blank to a face plate and rough-turn to the shape of the ring as shown in Fig. 5-22. Make 45° angular cuts before rounding in order to insure a true circular section.

3. Prepare an inside chuck over which the ring blank may be placed.

4. Remove the ring blank from the face plate and force it over the chuck.

5. Make remaining cuts on the ring to produce the circular section.

6. Sand and finish as desired.

§ X: Metal Spinning

Sheet metal disks may be formed into many shapes in a lathe by gradually forcing them over a metal or wood form or chuck, which revolves with the disk. This is done by means of pressure applied with a lubricated blunt-nosed wood or metal tool. Gold, silver, pewter, and aluminum in the thinner gauges can be spun without annealing (softening by heating). Copper, brass, bronze, iron, and Monel metal can be spun, but frequent annealing is necessary to keep the metal in a soft condition.

Spinning may be done on a metal lathe although the maximum speed of metal lathes is usually below the speed of a standard spinning lathe. A wood-turning lathe, which is built solidly enough to withstand the end thrust imposed by the forming process, will give good results. Roughly, the speed should be about 1000 rpm, varying with the metal and the diameter of the disk.

There are several essential tools or attachments used in spinning, which are not supplied with either the wood or metal lathe, but which can be purchased. They are discussed below:

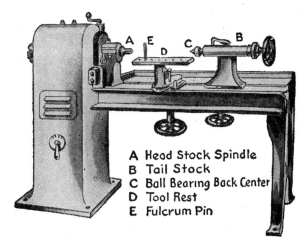

A **Head Stock Spindle**
B **Tail Stock**
C **Ball Bearing Back Center**
D **Tool Rest**
E **Fulcrum Pin**

FIG. 5-23   Metal-spinning lathe.

The Chuck. It is necessary to buy or make a chuck of metal or hard wood, whose outside contour is shaped to the exact inside contour of the spun article. The chuck must be provided with a threaded portion to screw onto the lathe spindle or it can be fastened to a faceplate. It is important to have this chuck run true so that the spun article will be perfectly symmetrical. In fact, it is impossible to spin unless the chuck does run true. If the craftsman turns the hard wood chucks himself, he can make his own designs, which adds much interest and personal satisfaction to the work.

When spinning a deep dish or vase, it is often necessary to make a series of molds, each one of the series being progressively nearer to the desired shape of the spun article. It is possible to spin articles which have a neck smaller than the bottom by the use of a chuck made in sections which will come apart when it is necessary to remove it from the spun metal.

The Back Center. The metal disk from which the article is spun is held on to the chuck by means of a special support or spinning center held in the tailstock. This support consists of two parts, a *follow block*, which is a piece of hard wood about $\frac{1}{2}''$ thick, turned down to a diameter a little smaller than the bottom of the article being spun, and a bearing, preferably a ball bearing assembly, to allow the follow block to rotate with the metal while it is being held against the chuck.

There are several commercial ball bearing back centers available for home work-shop wood lathes. (See Fig. 5-24).

The follow block may be held on the point of the dead center, or on a special dead center which has a pin in place of the 60° center. In this case, a hole to fit the pin is made in the follow block with a Forstner bit. A convenient and efficient

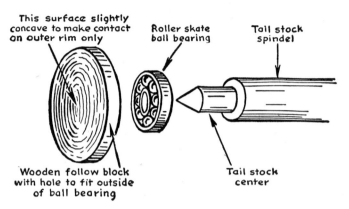

FIG. 5-24   The back center.

ball bearing center may be made by holding a roller skate bearing on the dead center, the outside of which fits a hole in the follow block. The follow block is usually slightly concave on the side which is against the metal. A little rosin will help to keep the disk from slipping.

The Tool Rest. The support for the spinning tool consists of a flat horizontal bar of iron supported in the rest holder of the lathe at a height slightly below the

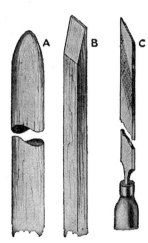

FIG. 5-25   Spinning tools.

center of the disk. Holes are bored in this bar at intervals of about 1″ for the purpose of inserting a steel pin, which acts as a fulcrum for the spinning tool. The fulcrum pin should be shouldered, in order to prevent it from falling through the hole in the bar. It is convenient to have two of these pins because in the process of spinning, it is some-times necessary to use two spinning tools at the same time.

Spinning Tools. For the beginner, a hard wood dowel stick or a broom handle, pointed as shown in the diagram, and a *back* stick, with a flat beveled end, are sufficient for the soft metals. These sticks should be about $2\frac{1}{2}'$ long, and about 1″ in diameter. A file sharpened as shown makes a handy trimming tool. There are available, sets of metal spinning tools which in the hands of an experienced spin-ner will do the work quickly and nicely, but wooden tools are preferable for the beginner. These tools must be kept in good condition, smooth, with no sharp edges to cut or mar the surface of the metal.

Procedure:

1. Place a properly formed chuck and follow block in position. The tailstock should be lined up with the headstock.

2. The disk or blank (aluminum or pewter about 20 gauge for beginners) is inserted between the chuck and the follow block. The blank should be large enough but not too large. No set rule for dimensions is possible. A simple method of finding the approximate disk radius is to measure with a string along the contour of the chuck, from the center of the bottom to the edge. Place enough pressure on the follow block to hold the metal disk firmly in place; do not use more pressure than is necessary. Center the disk as well as possible by eye.

Fig. 5-26   Holding the beveled stick. See (4) in Spinning Procedure.

3. Stand out of line with the disk, and start the lathe at a slow speed. If the disk is not too badly off center, it will revolve with the chuck and follow block. If it is too far off center, it may fly out with some force. *This is the most dangerous step in the spinning process, and caution is necessary.*

4. If the disk is running off center, hold the beveled stick as shown, so that it is in contact with the edge of the revolving disk and the tool rest. Release a little pressure from the follow block, at the same time applying a steady pressure with the beveled stick. This will cause the disk to center itself, after which the pressure

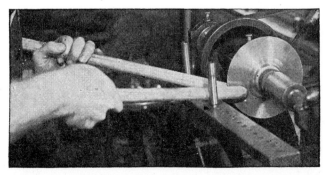

Fig. 5-27   Using back stick. See (6) in Spinning Procedure.

on the follow block is brought back to normal and the tailstock clamp tightened.

5. Stop the lathe and apply a suitable lubricant to the face of the disk. Heavy grease or tallow will give good results.

6. The pointed spinning tool is held under the right arm and close to the body. It is supported on the rest and against the pin, so as to obtain the necessary pressure against the metal disk. The rest is placed out from the disk just far enough to obtain the necessary leverage, and yet leave enough room to manipulate the tool end without cramping. The side of the point is brought against the revolving disk at a point just below, and tangent to the follow block, and pressure

Fig. 5-28   Trimming with a sharpened file.

is exerted with a *downward rolling and sliding motion*. The disk is thus forced slowly on to the chuck. It is good practice to make sure the disk is forced on or seated at the bottom of the chuck before the outer portions are touched. The disk must be forced on with long smooth strokes, using more pressure close to the chuck and less as the disk edge is reached. Make sure that each stroke is continuous to the edge of the disk. If the disk has a tendency to wrinkle, the back stick may be used in the other hand, and supported by another fulcrum pin, to apply pressure on the other side. This backing-up action will help to prevent, or will remove the wrinkles. However, with a little practice, it is entirely possible to spin the entire article with the pointed tool without wrinkles.

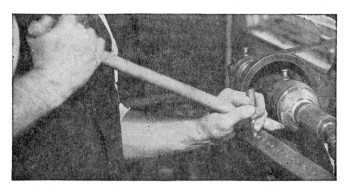

FIG. 5-29   Turning a bead with a back stick.

7. *Trimming.* This procedure is continued until the metal has been laid down firmly on the chuck up to within $\frac{1}{2}''$ of the edge of the metal. Turn the edge up to approximately a right angle for trimming. Before the final edge is laid down, the disk must be cut or trimmed true to the required size. The sharpened file is used for this operation. The file should be solidly supported on the rest as near to the point of cutting as possible. Watch out for the metal chips. It is advisable to wear goggles for this operation.

8. Now complete the spinning and polish with steel wool. A knurling tool can be used to form a decorative effect on the edge or on the outside. With a little practice, it is possible to turn a burr or a bead on the edge. In turning a burr the edge is turned over at an angle of about 90°. In turning the bead, the trimmed edge is not laid down but with the aid of the back stick is turned over on the metal to form a closed rounded edge.

§ XI: Back Rest

When turning a long piece in the lathe which has a tendency to vibrate because of slenderness, it is good practice to use a back rest. This is an accessory which may be supplied with the lathe only on special order. It consists of a supporting column, similar to the tool-rest support, on the back side of the lathe. On top of this column is a horizontal arm which usually has two rollers similar to roller-skate wheels that act as supports for the piece being turned. This arm is adjustable and is used by turning a straight place on the piece to be supported. Then bring the two wheels in contact with the work with a slight pressure to keep the piece from vibrating. This will enable the operator to work, as usual, from the front side of the piece with the two wheels on the back rest supporting the piece. Usually, this accessory is enough to support the pieces on long turning such as balusters, long handles, floor lamps, and other projects that tend to vibrate. Sometimes in preparing work for the back rest, it is almost impossible to stop the piece from vibrating, but if the hand is used as a support after the corners have been roughed off, one can usually succeed in getting a place smooth enough for the rollers. A home-made back rest could very well be made out of roller-skate wheels, but sometimes just a forked stick is used, with grease applied to reduce the friction.

VI

Projects

1. Taper Lamp
2. The Turned Wooden Mallet
3. Darning Ball
4. Gavel
5. Drawer Pulls
6. Windmill with a Turned Base
7. Candlestick
8. Turned Nut Bowl
9. Salt and Pepper Shakers
10. Circular End Table
11. Napkin Rings
12. Powder Box
13. Goblet and Ring
14. Shamrock Tray
15. Twin Ball Book Rack
16. Bridge Lamp
17. Spiral Lamp
18. Plastic Candlestick
19. Spun Lamp Base
20. Keene's Cement Turned Box with Lid
21. Floor Lamp
22. End Table
23. Lazy Susan
24. Turned Picture Frames
25. Scalloped Candy Dish
26. Cheese and Cracker Tray
27. Tilt-top Table
28. Keene's Cement Table Lamp
29. Colonial Table Lamp
30. Bridge Lamp

1. TAPER LAMP

The taper lamp, as shown in the drawing, should be made in pairs for use at the ends of the couch. This project represents a fundamental operation in wood-turning. The lamps can be made of mahogany, knotty pine, or any other wood that seasons well. In the drawing they are in the shape of a tapered piece. These lamps can be given a natural finish with a coat of shellac, then lacquer and wax, or with shellac and wax.

Materials Needed:

2 pc., 6″ square, 20″ long knotty pine
Fixtures for electrical connections

Procedure (see Fig. 6-1):

1. Set up one piece in the lathe on centers as described in Basic Operations.
2. Turn a cylinder with a diameter equal to the large diameter of the base.
3. Turn the dead center end down to the small diameter of the taper.
4. Turn the taper and sand.
5. Bore the hole as per Basic Operations with the drill in the headstock chuck, and the center hole of the lamp on the dead center. Drill from both ends and, if necessary, finish by hand with an auger bit.
6. If the lamps are top-heavy, they may be weighted by boring holes in the base which can be filled with molten lead.
7. Finish as desired.
8. Install electrical fittings.

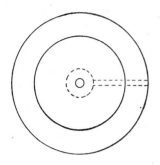

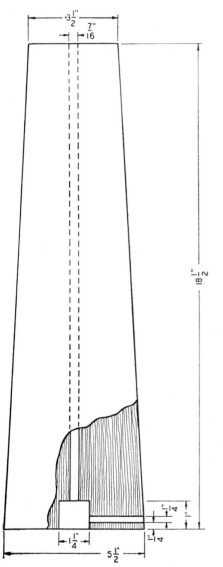

FIG. 6-1(a).

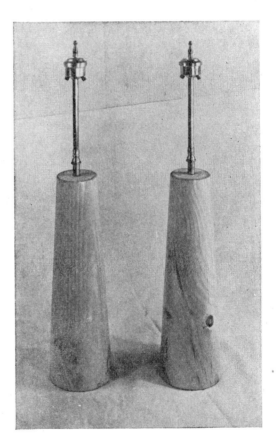

FIG. 6-1(b).

65

2. THE TURNED WOODEN MALLET

A wooden mallet is a valuable tool for the kit of a home workshop and can easily be made by the method described. The head of the mallet should be a hard, firm, non-splitting wood such as elm, maple, or lignum vitae. Hickory is an excellent wood for the handle, although oak, ash, or birch can be used.

Materials Needed:

1 pc., Head #1:	$4'' \times 4'' \times 7\frac{1}{2}''$	maple
1 pc., Handle #1:	$2'' \times 2'' \times 14\frac{1}{2}''$	hickory

Procedure (see Fig. 6-2):

Head:

1. Set up in the lathe on centers the piece of $4'' \times 4''$ maple as indicated in the Materials Needed list.

2. Turn down to a cylinder $\frac{1}{16}''$ larger than the largest diameter.

3. Mark center longitudinally with a skew chisel and lay off correct length on each side of the center mark.

4. Cut face of mallet down, leaving a remainder about $1''$ in diameter. Note that the face is slightly convex.

5. Turn the head according to the drawing.

6. Sand and finish.

7. Take out of lathe and cut off each end $\frac{1}{16}''$ long. Smooth these down with a file. Polish, and shellac.

8. To locate the hole for the handle, obtain a strip of paper long enough to go around the mallet in the middle section. Wrap the paper around the mallet head so that the ends of the paper meet at any given point. This point should then be marked on the mallet head.

9. Remove the paper from the mallet head; fold in half to find the mid-point. Wrap the paper again around the mallet head, making sure that the ends are on the layout mark. Mark off the opposite point at the fold of the paper.

10. Set the faces in the vise and, with auger bit, bore halfway through from each side. Note that the hole for the handle should be bored at right angles to the slashed grain to reduce the possibility of splitting.

Handle:

1. Mount the piece of stock for the handle in the lathe on centers.

2. Turn down to the largest diameter.

3. Make the layout, with the small end toward the tailstock.

4. Turn small end and test for size with the hole in the mallet head. Turn rest of handle as per drawing.

5. Sand thoroughly.

6. Remove from lathe and saw slot for wedge at right angles to the slashed grain about $1\frac{1}{2}''$ deep.

7. Make wedge of hardwood.

8. Drive handle into mallet head. Note sawed slot at right angles to the grain of the wood in the head of the mallet. Put glue on wedge. Drive in hard.

9. Flatten the sides of the handle with a plane while gripping the faces of the mallet in the vise. Smooth with file and sandpaper.

10. Saw excess stock from both ends and sand.

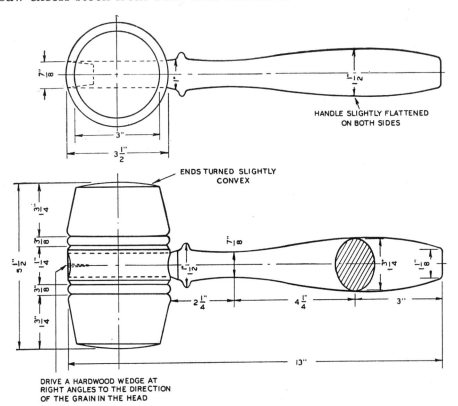

FIG. 6-2(a).

FIG. 6-2(b).

3. DARNING BALL

A darning ball is a useful accessory for the sewing basket. Either of the suggested designs may be selected or you may elect to design one of your own. This project offers practice in the most elementary spindle turning.

Material Needed:

1 pc., 2″ × 2″ × 7″ maple

Procedure (see Fig. 6-3):

1. Center the ends of the stock for spindle turning.
2. Mount the work between centers in the lathe.
3. Turn a cylindrical shape $1\frac{7}{8}''$ diameter.
4. Lay off locations of diameters shown on the drawing.
5. With parting tool turn sizing cuts as indicated.
6. Turn handle and ball to shape.
7. Sand and apply French polish.
8. Remove the work from the lathe, trim, and finish the ends.

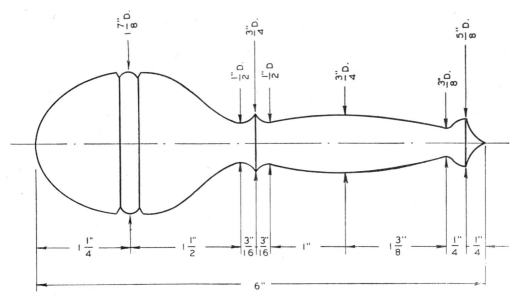

FIG. 6-3(a).

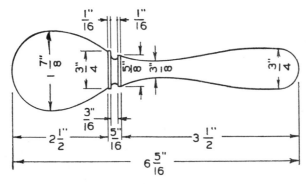

ALTERNATE DESIGN

FIG. 6-3(b).

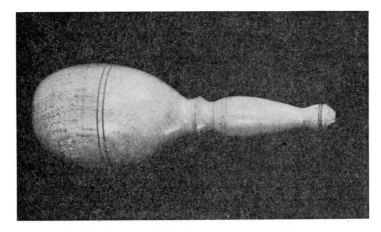

FIG. 6-3(c).

69

4. GAVEL

This is a very interesting article to make on the wood lathe. It affords the beginner some good practice in the techniques of wood-turning and results in a useful and ornamental product. A great variety of original designs may be used and only small pieces of wood are required. The one described below was made with a walnut head and a contrasting maple handle. Any hardwood that turns nicely will serve.

Materials Needed:

1 pc., head block:	$2'' \times 2'' \times 5''$	walnut
1 pc., handle:	$\frac{3}{4}'' \times \frac{3}{4}'' \times 9''$	maple

Procedure (see Fig. 6-4):

1. Prepare the block for the head to the above dimensions and mount it between centers.
2. Turn the block to a cylinder of $1\frac{3}{4}''$ diameter.
3. Lay out the distances for the surface curves.
4. Turn the head to the shape indicated. Be sure to locate the "V" groove in the exact center of the head and make parting cuts at both faces to a diameter of about $\frac{1}{4}''$.
5. Sand carefully and finish with a French polish.
6. Remove from centers, cut off waste stock, and finish the faces.
7. Locate a point in the "V" groove which will be the center of the handle hole. This point should be chosen so that the handle hole will be perpendicular to the slash grain to help prevent splitting.
8. Cut a strip of paper about $\frac{1}{4}''$ wide and long enough to reach around the head.
9. Wrap the strip around the head, starting with one end of the strip at the handle-hole center-mark previously located.
10. Mark off on the strip the exact distance of the head circumference of the handle position.
11. Cut the strip to this length and fold in half.
12. Now use this folded strip to locate the center of the handle hole which will be diametrically opposite to the original center-mark.
13. Bore the $\frac{3}{8}''$ handle hole by boring in toward the axis from each of the centers just located.
14. Mount the handle piece between centers and turn to indicated dimensions. The handle dowel must be slightly tapered and carefully fitted to the hole in the head. Make a parting cut at the handle end.
15. Sand and finish.
16. Remove from the lathe and cut off waste stock.
17. Saw a slot in the dowel to a distance of about $\frac{3}{4}''$ and make a wedge to drive into it. The wedge must have just enough thickness to insure a permanently tight handle.
18. Assemble, drive and trim off the wedge.

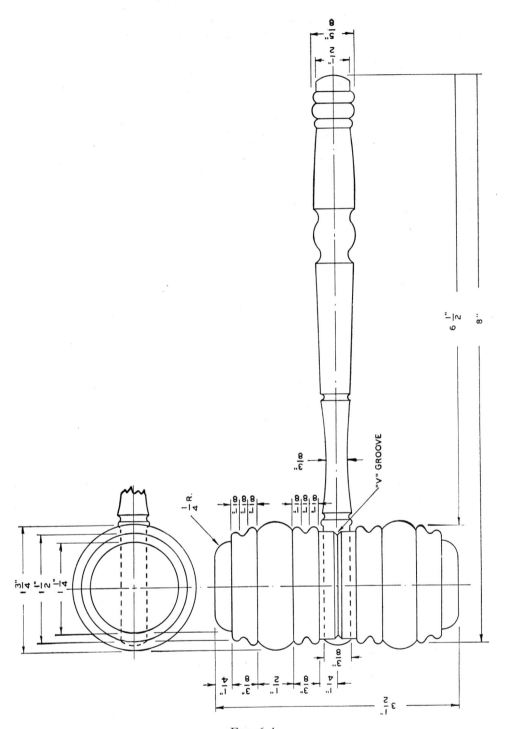

FIG. 6-4.

5. DRAWER PULLS

Drawer pulls often become broken in the home. It is a comparatively simple job to turn a new one which matches the one which was broken. Sets of drawer pulls may also be made for articles of furniture constructed at home.

Materials Needed:

(Kind and size to be chosen as desired)

Procedure (see Fig. 6-5):

1. Prepare a suitable-sized block from which the drawer pull is to be turned.
2. Mount the block on the screw center. The screw center used must not be larger than the drawer pull screw which will hold the drawer pull on the drawer. The block may be mounted so that the center screw goes into either the end or the slash grain.
3. Turn the block to shape. See Fig. 6-5.
4. Sand and finish as desired.
5. Bore the correct size hole for the drawer pull screw that is being used.

Alternate Method for Matched Drawer Pulls:

1. Prepare a block long enough to turn the desired number of pulls. Allow for the parting tool cuts and end waste. (See diagram.)
2. Mount the block between centers.
3. Turn the set of drawer pulls to size, making the parting tool cuts to about $\frac{1}{4}''$ diameter.
4. Sand and finish as desired.
5. Remove work from centers and saw the separate pulls apart. Sand and finish the parting cuts.
6. Drill a pilot hole for the drawer pull screws.

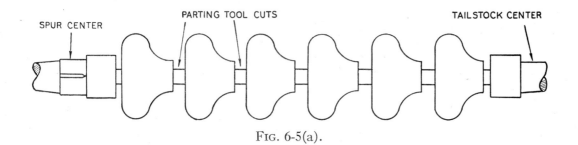

SPUR CENTER   PARTING TOOL CUTS   TAILSTOCK CENTER

FIG. 6-5(a).

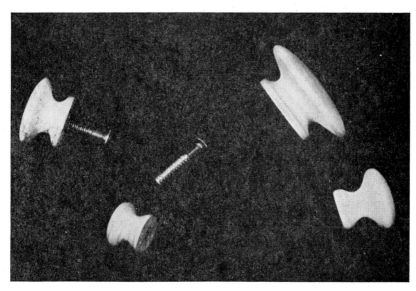

FIG. 6-5(b).

6. WINDMILL WITH A TURNED BASE

This is an interesting and practical project to be used as a weather-vane. It involves two fundamental operations in wood-turning, namely, that of taper turning and turning a semi-sphere.

Materials Needed:

1 pc., base:	$5\frac{1}{2}'' \times 5\frac{1}{2}'' \times 13''$	pine
1 pc., fan support dowel:	$\frac{3}{4}'' \times 3\frac{1}{2}''$	birch
4 pc., spokes:	$\frac{3}{8}'' \times 8\frac{1}{4}''$	birch
12 pc., fan vanes:	$\frac{3}{16}'' \times 1\frac{1}{2}'' \times 3''$	basswood
1 pc., tail base:	$\frac{3}{4}'' \times 1\frac{1}{4}'' \times 14''$	pine
1 pc., tail disk:	$\frac{3}{4}'' \times 5''$ dia.	pine
1 pc., tail dowel:	$\frac{3}{8}'' \times 13''$	birch
1 pc., hub:	$1'' \times 2\frac{1}{2}''$ dia.	maple

Procedure (see Fig. 6-6):

Base:

1. Secure a piece of soft pine 13'' long and $5\frac{1}{2}''$ square. Rough off the corners and prepare this for turning between centers.

2. Set up in the lathe on centers and turn down to a cylinder 5'' in diameter.

3. Lay out the length of the spherical section which is to form the top of the windmill adding $\frac{1}{2}''$ for dead center. You will note that the diameters of the top and base are the same.

4. With a parting tool, cut in for the top of the tapered portion of the body, and turn the taper as indicated.

5. Turn the spherical top. Leave as little as possible to be cut off by hand.

6. Use a parting tool to square the face at proper length, making sure that this cut is carried in at right angles to the axis.

7. Sand smoothly and give a coat of shellac. Remove from the lathe and cut off dead center piece.

8. After sawing off the projection on the base, smooth carefully and locate the position of the dowel which holds the windmill fan.

9. Bore in with an auger bit for a distance of 2'' and insert and glue the $\frac{3}{4}''$ fan dowel.

Fan:

You will note that the hub of the fan is also a turned piece. This can be turned on a screw center to the dimensions as indicated.

10. Bore the holes for the spokes.

11. Cut out the vanes.

12. Assemble the vanes on the spokes. These are usually fastened on with small flathead nails.

13. Assemble the fan.

74

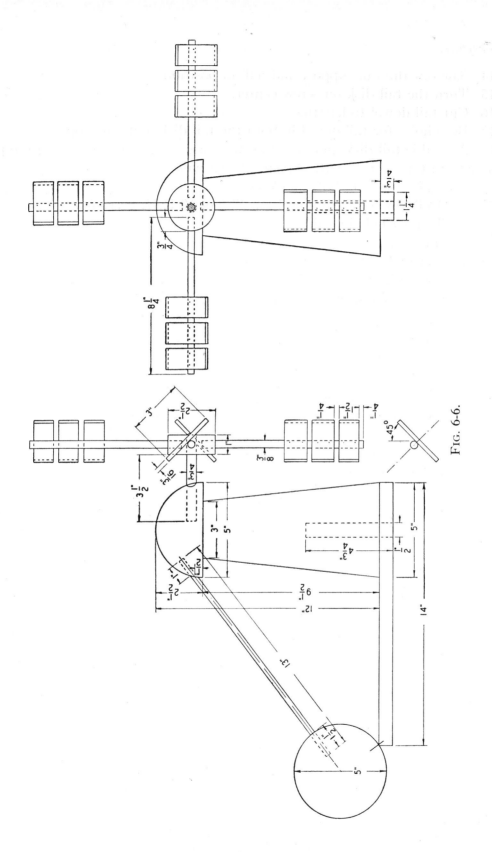

Fig. 6-6.

75

Tailpiece:

14. Saw out the tail support and nail in position.
15. Turn the tail disk on screw center.
16. Cut tail dowel to length.
17. Bore holes for tail dowel in both the tail disk and base top.
18. Assemble tail disk and dowel on tail base by gluing into the base top and fastening to tail support with 8-penny finish nail.
19. Bore pivot hole in bottom of base.
20. Drill pilot hole in fan dowel for 2″ No. 10 R.H. brass fan screw.
21. Drill shank hole in hub.
22. Put on fan.
23. Inspect and sand for smoothness.
24. Shellac with orange shellac.
25. Paint as desired. Suggested colors:

Base	white bottom, red sphere
Tail supporter	dark green
Tail disk	red
Tail dowel	white
Fan support dowel	red
Fan hub	dark green
Fan spokes	white
Fan vanes, inside and outside	red
Fan vanes, middle	white

7. CANDLESTICK

The candlestick described here is an interesting project for the beginner. It involves both spindle and face-plate turning. If a pair of candlesticks is desired, the craftsman will gain experience in turning duplicate parts. This project may also be adapted to make a small table lamp.

Materials Needed:

1 pc., candleholder:	$2'' \times 2'' \times 6''$	white pine
1 pc., base:	$2'' \times 6'' \times 6''$	white pine
1 pc., plug:	$1'' \times 1'' \times 1\frac{1}{2}''$	white pine

Procedure (see Fig. 6-7):

1. Lay out the centers on the candleholder as described in Basic Operations.

2. On one end, bore a $\frac{3}{4}''$ hole, 1'' deep. This hole must then be plugged to receive the lathe center.

3. Mount the piece for the plug on the lathe and turn to $\frac{3}{4}''$ diameter. This plug must fit snugly in the hole of the candleholder.

4. Press the plug into the hole and mount the stock on the lathe, using the center hole of the plug for the dead center.

5. Turn to the required dimensions. Be sure that the tenon to fit into the base is exactly $\frac{3}{4}''$ in diameter. Make the tenon on the live center end of the stock.

6. Sand the candleholder while on the lathe.

7. Fasten the piece of stock for the base on a face plate and mount on the lathe as described in "Face Plate Turning," Basic Operations.

8. Turn to required dimensions.

9. Bore a hole $\frac{3}{4}''$ deep and $\frac{3}{4}''$ in diameter. This may be done with a skew chisel, or a square-nose tool while the work is revolving on the lathe. Care must be taken to make the hole of a size so that the tenon of the candleholder fits snugly.

10. Glue the candleholder into the base. This may be done by leaving the base mounted on the lathe. Apply a coat of glue to the tenon of the upright and press the tenon into the hole in the base. Run the dead center into the center hole in the end of the candleholder, forcing it tightly into the base so that the tail-stock spindle acts as a clamp. Allow to remain in this position overnight.

11. When the glue has dried, and with the dead center supporting the end of the candlestick, start the lathe and sand the entire project.

12. Apply French polish.

13. Remove the work from the lathe. Remove the face plate from the base, and remove the plug from the end of the candleholder.

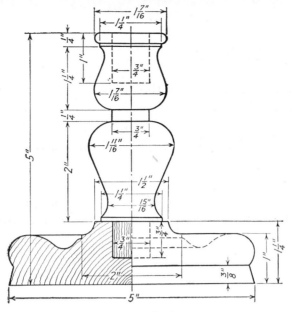

Fig. 6-7(a).

Fig. 6-7(b).

79

8. TURNED NUT BOWL

A simple, but beautiful, example of the art of face-plate turning is incorporated in this small nut bowl. The size is small enough to be turned from one piece of wood. Suggested shapes may be altered to suit the individual's taste; however, the beginner should keep within the suggested dimensions.

Materials Needed:

1 pc., bowl:	$2'' \times 6'' \times 6''$	maple
1 pc., face-plate block:	$\frac{3}{4}'' \times 6'' \times 6''$	white pine

Procedure (see Fig. 6-8):

1. Surface both faces of the face-plate block so that they are smooth, flat, and parallel.
2. Surface one face of the bowl blank so that it is smooth and perfectly flat.
3. Apply glue to one face of each piece, place a piece of heavy paper between these surfaces, and clamp them together. Allow the glue to dry overnight.
4. Remove the clamps and lay out the largest possible circle on one surface.
5. Band-saw the blank to this line. (If a band saw is not available, cut off corners at a 45° angle and tangent to the layout circle.)
6. Fasten the face plate to the face-plate block with suitable woodscrews.
7. Screw the face plate onto the headstock spindle and arrange the tool rest in place for turning the outside.
8. Turn the outside to shape.
9. Readjust the tool rest and turn the inside of the bowl. (Test for thickness using the thumb and index finger as a gauge.)
10. Sandpaper carefully.
11. Apply a French polish.
12. Remove the bowl from the face-plate block, using a wide chisel and mallet. Hold the chisel edge on the paper joint, bevel toward the waste stock, and strike a sharp blow with the mallet.
13. Glue a piece of felt to the bottom, or flock the bottom with rayon flocking material.

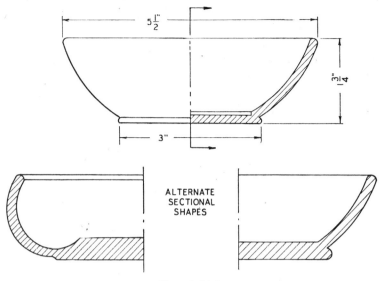

5 1/2"

3"

3/4"

ALTERNATE
SECTIONAL
SHAPES

Fig. 6-8(a).

Fig. 6-8(b).

Fig. 6-8(c).

9. SALT AND PEPPER SHAKERS

A set of these novelty salt and pepper shakers not only affords the turner an excellent example of duplicate spindle turning, but also will make an attractive table piece. There are many designs which may be used for this project. Either of the three suggested designs may be chosen or the turner may wish to sketch a design of his own. In order to be sure that the hole in the bottom of each shaker is exactly centered, the hole is first bored in the rough stock and plugs are turned to fit into these holes. This method of turning is known as plug turning and will produce work which is concentric with these center holes.

Materials Needed:

1 pc., shakers:	$2'' \times 2'' \times 6''$	maple
1 pc., plugs:	$1'' \times 1'' \times 4''$	maple
2 pc., washers:	$\frac{7}{8}'' \text{ D} \times \frac{3}{16}''$	birch dowel

Procedure (see Fig. 6-9):

1. Locate the centers on both ends of the shaker blank.
2. Bore the $\frac{7}{8}''$ D hole to a depth of $2''$ from each end of blank. (A $\frac{7}{8}''$ twist drill or No. 14 Forstner bit may be used either in the drill press or brace, whichever is available for this job.)
3. Center the plug blank for spindle turning.
4. Turn the plugs slightly tapered with the large end of the plugs at the outside ends.
5. Cut off the plug $1''$ from each end.
6. Force each plug into the $\frac{7}{8}''$ hole in the shaker blank. (Do not destroy the marks for the spur and cup center on the plugs since these will be used later.)
7. Using the plug center marks, mount the shaker blank between centers.
8. Turn down to $1\frac{7}{8}''$ diameter throughout.
9. Face each end slightly concave.
10. Lay out exact length of shaker from each end.
11. Cut in at this point to about $\frac{1}{2}''$ D with a parting tool.
12. Turn the shakers to shape.
13. With the point of the skew chisel, cut a "V" groove as indicated on the drawing. (Leave enough material to support the work while it is being sanded.)
14. Sand the work and apply a French polish.
15. Remove the work from the lathe and saw the shakers apart. Pull out the plugs by gripping the plug in the vise.
16. Make two wooden washers by boring a $\frac{7}{16}''$ hole in the center of a length of $\frac{7}{8}''$ dowel and sawing off two $\frac{3}{16}''$ pieces from the end.
17. Lay out and drill the holes for the salt and pepper.
18. Sand these washers and glue them in place.
19. Sand the top ends carefully and apply two light coats of shellac.

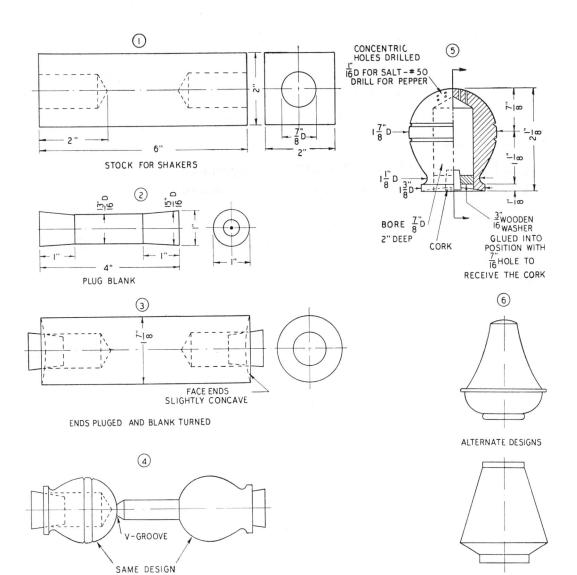

① STOCK FOR SHAKERS

2"

6"

2"

2"

$\frac{7}{8}$" D

② PLUG BLANK

$\frac{13}{16}$" D

$\frac{15}{16}$" D

1"

1"

4"

1"

③ ENDS PLUGED AND BLANK TURNED

$\frac{7}{8}$"

FACE ENDS
SLIGHTLY CONCAVE

④

V-GROOVE

SAME DESIGN

⑤ CONCENTRIC
HOLES DRILLED
$\frac{1}{16}$" D FOR SALT – # 50
DRILL FOR PEPPER

$1\frac{7}{8}$" D

$1\frac{1}{8}$" D

$1\frac{3}{8}$" D

BORE $\frac{7}{8}$" D
2" DEEP

CORK

$\frac{7}{8}$"

$2\frac{1}{8}$"

$1\frac{1}{8}$"

$\frac{1}{8}$"

$\frac{3}{16}$" WOODEN
WASHER
GLUED INTO
POSITION WITH
$\frac{7}{16}$" HOLE TO
RECEIVE THE CORK

⑥ ALTERNATE DESIGNS

FIG. 6-9(a).

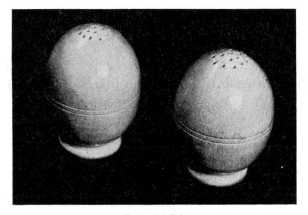

FIG. 6-9(b).

83

10. CIRCULAR END TABLE

This end table may be used as an occasional table or the dimensions may be changed to meet the needs of a coffee table. It may be made from any kind of wood and finished to any taste. Maple, birch, and sycamore are very popular.

Materials Needed:

3 pc., legs:	2″ × 2″ × 31″	sycamore
1 pc., top:	1¼″ × 24″ × 24″	sycamore

Procedure (see Fig. 6-10):

1. Turn legs between centers. The end diameters are ¾″ and the diameter of the center of the leg is 2″. The legs are 31″ in length and the profile is a gradual convex curve from end to end. A ¾″ × 1¼″ dowel should be turned on one end of each leg.

2. Sand and finish each leg in the lathe. A French polish, using white shellac, makes a very fine natural finish.

3. The top may be band-sawed from a solid piece of wood. You may, in all probability, have to glue several 1¼″ × 24″ pieces together edge to edge to obtain the desired diameter of 24″. If no band saw is available, the top may be turned on the lathe (see outboard turning in Basic Operations). Trim as many corners from the top as possible with a hand saw before mounting on outside of headstock and run the lathe as slow as possible. The top may also be finished while it is on the face plate.

4. Lay out position of legs on underside of top. Scribe a 20″ circle. Divide the circumference of the circle into three equal parts. Prick-punch the center for each dowel hole 1″ to the right of each division mark. This is necessary in order to have the theoretical vertical center line of the table pass through the crossed legs (see bottom view in drawing).

5. Bore a ¾″ hole, 1¼″ deep, into each prick-punched position. The brace and bit should be held at a 45° angle. A jig, made by boring a 45° hole through a 2″ × 4″, would be very helpful in this operation.

6. Glue each leg into place.

7. The legs may be screwed together where they cross each other. The screws should be counter-bored and the screw holes plugged with matching wood.

8. Trim the bottom of each leg. (See trim line in drawing.)

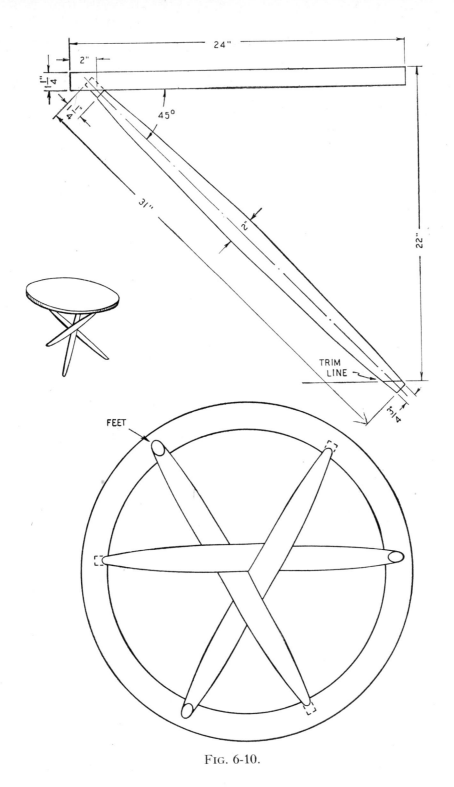

24"

2"

$1\frac{1}{4}$"

4$\frac{1}{2}$"

45°

31"

2"

22"

TRIM
LINE

3$\frac{1}{4}$

FEET

FIG. 6-10.

85

11. NAPKIN RINGS

Napkin rings are practical and decorative articles and are easy to make on the home workshop lathe. Pieces of wood which might otherwise be discarded may be utilized for this project. A great variety of designs and of different kinds of wood may be used. The ones described below were turned from mahogany.

Materials Needed:

2 pc., blocks: $2'' \times 2\frac{1}{2}'' \times 2\frac{1}{2}''$ mahogany

Procedure (see Fig. 6-11):

1. Cut out or glue together suitable blocks.
2. Lay out a $2\frac{1}{4}''$ circle on one end of the blocks and cut away most of the waste stock.
3. Mount the block on a screw center and turn the outside to the desired shape. Leave enough stock on the screw center side for the cutting off process.
4. Sand and finish the outside surface.
5. Bore out the interior as shown in Fig. 6-11.
6. Sand interior surface.
7. Cut off with parting tool.
8. Sand the edge just cut off by hand. Finish this end and the interior surface.

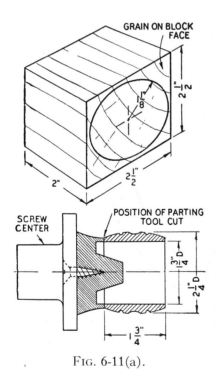

FIG. 6-11(a).

FIG. 6-11(b).

12. POWDER BOX

Many useful and ornamental boxes of various designs may be made on the wood lathe. The stock for the box may be a solid block or may be glued up from thinner pieces. Interesting decorative effects may be produced by gluing up a block consisting of contrasting layers of wood.

Materials Needed:

1 pc., box block:	$3'' \times 5'' \times 5''$	mahogany
1 pc., cover block:	$1\frac{5}{8}'' \times 5'' \times 5''$	mahogany

Procedure (see Fig. 6-12):

1. Prepare the box block. The bottom surface must be smooth and flat.
2. Lay out a $4\frac{7}{8}''$ circle on the bottom. Plainly mark the center of this circle.
3. Cut out a $4\frac{7}{8}''$ disk from the block on the band saw.
4. Mount this disk on a face plate so that the axes of the face plate and of the disk correspond closely.
5. Turn the block to dimensions indicated.
6. Sand and finish the box as desired. Do not remove from face plate.
7. Mount the cover block on a second face plate, using a procedure similar to that used in mounting the box block.
8. Turn the inside surface of the cover. Also turn the complete rim. The lip of the rim must be fitted to the inside of the box rim so that box acts as an outside chuck.
9. Sand the turned portion of the cover, being careful not to touch the lip. Remove it from the face plate and mount it on the completed box, using the box as a chuck.
10. Complete the turning of the cover.
11. Sand and finish as desired.
12. The chucking lip may now be sanded by hand to assure a loose fit.
13. Remove box from the face plate and glue a piece of felt to the bottom.

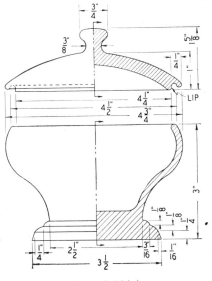

FIG. 6-12(a)

FIG. 6-12(b).

13. GOBLET AND RING

The loose ring on this turning is too small to be taken off at either end. Although it is of no practical use, it will mystify and delight your friends. The bowl of the goblet may be used as a nut or bon-bon dish. The nature of this project makes it necessary for the turner to have mastered the fundamentals of face-plate turning before attempting to make it. Strict attention should also be paid to the correct order of procedure if the turning is to be successful.

Materials Needed:

1 pc., $3\frac{1}{4}''$ × $3\frac{1}{4}''$ × $5\frac{1}{4}''$ maple

Procedure (see Fig. 6-13):

1. Square one end of the stock so that it is at right angles to two adjacent surfaces.
2. Fasten a face plate to this end of the stock and support the outer end with the tailstock center.
3. Rough-turn the outside to a 3″ diameter cylinder.
4. Remove the tailstock center and turn the inside of the goblet.
5. Partially shape the outside, leaving material for the ring. (See B, Fig. 6-13.)
6. Shape outside of ring.
7. Under-cut the ring from left and right with offset tools made by bending and grinding the tang of an old file. (Do not cut the ring loose. Leave enough material to hold the ring while it is being sanded.)
8. Sand and apply a French polish to the ring.
9. Cut the ring loose with one of the offset tools.
10. Finish turning the stem. Hold the ring in one hand while turning the stem so that the ring does not get caught on the tool.
11. Sand the goblet and apply a French polish.
12. Cut off the goblet at its base with a parting tool. Support the outer end of the goblet with the left hand as the parting tool cut is being completed.
13. Cement a piece of felt on the bottom if desired.

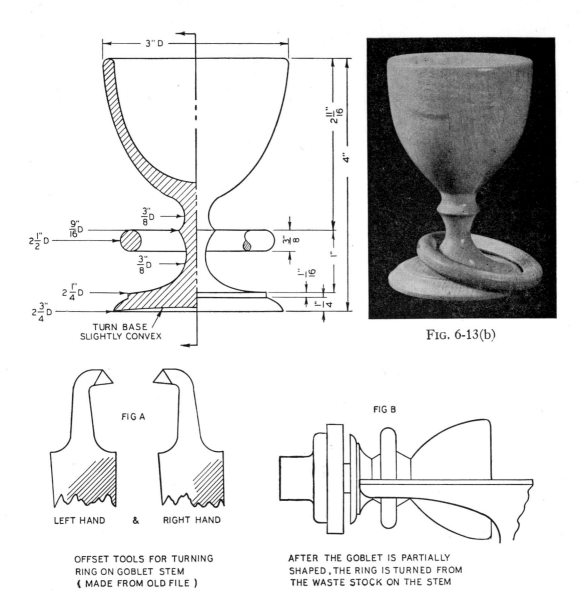

3" D

2 11/16"

4"

9/16" D

2 1/2" D

3/8" D

3/8" D

3" 8

1"

2 1/4" D

1" 16

2 3/4" D

1" 4

TURN BASE
SLIGHTLY CONVEX

FIG. 6-13(b)

FIG A

LEFT HAND   &   RIGHT HAND

OFFSET TOOLS FOR TURNING
RING ON GOBLET STEM
(MADE FROM OLD FILE)

FIG B

AFTER THE GOBLET IS PARTIALLY
SHAPED, THE RING IS TURNED FROM
THE WASTE STOCK ON THE STEM

FIG. 6-13(a).

89

14. SHAMROCK TRAY

This project might be classified as "trick turning." It will stimulate the imagination of one who is familiar with ordinary methods of wood turning. The depressions in this tray are turned on four separate centers. The effect of this treatment leaves a pleasing design in the tray. Since the piece is to be mounted off center, one must be sure that the blank will "swing" over the bed of the lathe in each position in which it is to be mounted. The design shown here will swing on a lathe built to take a 10″ turning. *Caution:* Mounting work off center is dangerous unless extreme precaution is taken to fasten the work securely and also to use the slowest available speed.

Materials Needed:

1 pc., tray:	1″ × 6″ × 7″	mahogany
1 pc., face-plate block:	¾″ × 6″ × 7″	pine

Procedure (see Fig. 6-14):

1. Surface each face of the face-plate block and the tray piece so that they are perfectly smooth, flat, and parallel.

2. Carefully lay out the design of the shamrock on the tray blank with dividers. Be sure that the centers are clearly marked on the blank at A, B, C, and O.

3. Saw out the outer contour of the shamrock carefully on either the jig saw or band saw.

4. Trace the outline of this piece on the face-plate block and cut this out also.

5. Apply glue to one side of each piece and glue the pieces together with a piece of heavy paper inserted between the blocks. Carefully line up the outer edges of the blanks and clamp until the glue is dry.

6. Place a small (3″ preferred) face plate on the lathe and position the work on the face plate, holding it in place by placing the point of the tailstock center at the point "O" on the work. This procedure in locating the work on the face plate will assure correct centering.

7. Clamp the work piece to the face plate in this position with a "C" clamp. Unscrew this face-plate assembly from the lathe spindle and fasten the face-plate block to the face plate with ¾″ No. 10 flathead woodscrews.

8. Turn the center depression ⅞″ deep and 2½″ diameter.

9. Sand this section carefully.

10. Using the same procedure for centering the blank, turn the depressions at A, B, and C. The depth of the depression in each case may be gauged by comparing it with the first depression turned. Sand each section carefully before proceeding to the next.

11. Carefully remove the tray from the face-plate block by splitting it off with a chisel at the paper joint. Place the edge of the chisel on the joint, bevel toward the waste block, and strike a sharp blow with the mallet.

12. Carefully file and sand all outer edges.

13. Apply finish as desired.

14. Cement a piece of felt on the bottom.

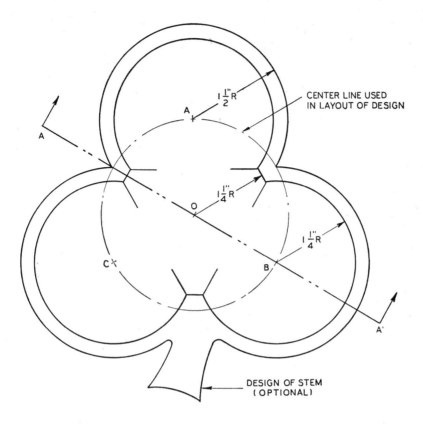

CENTER LINE USED
IN LAYOUT OF DESIGN

$1\frac{1}{2}''R$

$1\frac{1}{4}''R$

$1\frac{1}{4}''R$

DESIGN OF STEM
(OPTIONAL)

SECTION THROUGH A A'

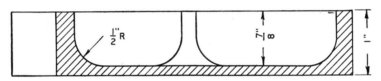

$\frac{1}{2}''R$

$\frac{7}{8}''$

$1''$

FIG. 6-14(a).

FIG. 6-14(b).

15. TWIN BALL BOOK RACK

This novel book rack provides several turning techniques and results in a very interesting accessory for room decoration. Although the balls appear to be resting on an inclined plane, they are actually fastened to a curtain rod and are adjustable.

Materials Needed:

2 pc., $4\frac{1}{4}'' \times 4\frac{1}{4}'' \times 6''$ mahogany for balls (these two pieces may be made by gluing-up stock)
2 pc., $\frac{1}{2}'' \times 1'' \times 7\frac{5}{8}''$ mahogany for split turnings
4 pc., $\frac{3}{8}'' \times 2'' \times 2''$ mahogany for turned rosettes or disks
1 pc., $1\frac{3}{8}'' \times 2\frac{1}{8}'' \times 16\frac{1}{4}''$ maple, or some other contrasting wood, for bottom
2 pc., $\frac{3}{4}'' \times 2\frac{3}{8}'' \times 18\frac{1}{2}''$ maple for sides
1 pc., $12''$ length of a section of curtain rod
2 pc., $\frac{1}{8}'' \times \frac{1}{2}'' \times \frac{3}{4}''$ pieces of metal filed to fit inside of curtain rod

Procedure (see Fig. 6-15):

1. Turn mahogany balls and finish natural with French polish (see friction chucks in Basic Operations).
2. Turn rosettes or disks on small face plate and finish natural with French polish.
3. Turn split turnings and finish natural with French polish before breaking apart (see split turnings in Basic Operations).
4. Band saw, or form by hand, the maple bottom according to the dimensions in the drawing. If you desire to do so, the bottom may be made from two pieces of $\frac{3}{4}'' \times 2\frac{1}{8}'' \times 8''$ maple. The two pieces may be fastened to the sides so that they taper toward the center of the book rack.
5. Band saw, or form by hand, the two sides as per the dimensions in the drawing.
6. Assemble the bottom and sides. They may be doweled together or fastened together with brads or glue. Finish natural, using white shellac.
7. Fasten split turnings and rosettes in place, using fine brads.
8. Place the length of curtain rod on the longitudinal center line of the base, open side up. Carefully bend into place and fasten to bottom with brass escutcheon pins. Screws may be used, but the heads should be countersunk.
9. Drill a screw hole through the center of each small metal slide and fasten one slide to each mahogany ball with a woodscrew. The screw should be countersunk.
10. Mount the balls on the curtain rod by inserting the metal slides into the ends of the rod and the book rack is ready for use. A piece of felt glued to the bottom will prevent the marring of furniture.

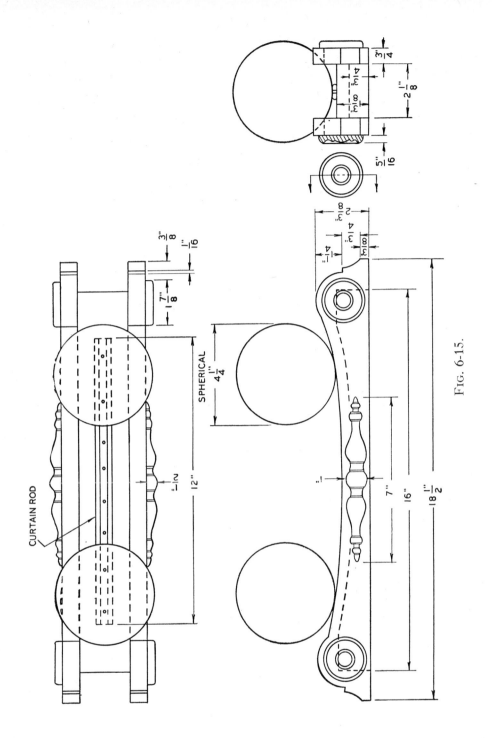

CURTAIN ROD

SPHERICAL

$4\frac{1}{4}$"

12"

$\frac{1}{2}$"

$\frac{3}{8}$"

$\frac{1}{16}$"

$1\frac{7}{8}$"

$2\frac{3}{8}$"

4"

$4\frac{1}{3}$"

$\frac{3}{8}$"

$1\frac{1}{2}$"

$\frac{1}{8}$"

7"

16"

$18\frac{1}{2}$"

$\frac{3}{4}$"

$4\frac{1}{3}$"

$\frac{1}{8}$"

$\frac{3}{8}$"

$2\frac{1}{8}$"

$\frac{5}{16}$"

Fig. 6-15.

93

16. BRIDGE LAMP

Either of the suggested styles of colonial bridge lamps may be turned from the accompanying drawings. The only difference between the two styles is in the angular hole drilled in the bracket arm and the method of attaching the socket. This lamp incorporates a good number of the fundamental techniques in faceplate, spindle and chuck turning. Birch, maple, and cherry would be excellent woods to use in its construction.

Materials Needed:

3 pc., legs:	$1\frac{1}{2}'' \times 1\frac{1}{2}'' \times 12''$	maple
1 pc., base:	$2'' \times 6\frac{5}{8}'' \times 6\frac{5}{8}''$	maple
1 pc., main spindle:	$2\frac{1}{4}'' \times 2\frac{1}{4}'' \times 17\frac{1}{2}''$	maple
1 pc., stem:	$1'' \times 1'' \times 30''$	maple
1 pc., bracket:	$2'' \times 2'' \times 12''$	maple
1 pc., candle cup:	$\frac{3}{4}'' \times 3\frac{1}{2}'' \times 3\frac{1}{2}''$	maple
1 pc., chuck block for above:	$\frac{3}{4}'' \times 3\frac{1}{2}'' \times 3\frac{1}{2}''$	pine
1 pc., finial:	$2'' \times 2'' \times 6''$	maple

$\frac{1}{8}''$ pipe nipple, socket, plug, and cord for wiring.

(*Note:* If the lamp is made of birch or maple, a $\frac{7}{8}''$ D dowel may be used for the stem. This will eliminate the turning of this long, slender piece.)

Procedure (see Fig. 6-16):

Legs:

1. Get out stock for legs. Center and turn these pieces to the dimensions indicated on the drawing. Take care to make the $\frac{7}{8}''$ D dowel ends accurately so that they will fit into the holes to be drilled into the base.
2. Sand and apply a French polish to the legs. Do not sand or apply finish to the dowel end.
3. Remove from the lathe and cut off ends to shape indicated in the drawing.

Base:

1. Plane one surface of the blank smooth and flat.
2. With a pair of dividers, lay out the largest possible circle on this face.
3. Lay out a $2\frac{3}{8}''$ radius circle from the same center as used above.
4. Mark out three equal divisions on this $2\frac{3}{8}''$ radius circle. These are the locations of the holes to receive the legs.
5. Bore a $\frac{7}{8}''$ D hole at an angle of 60° in a short piece of $2'' \times 4''$. This block will serve as a jig to help bore the leg holes at the correct angle.
6. With the aid of the above jig, bore the $\frac{7}{8}''$ leg holes as indicated.
7. Cut out the circular disk on the band saw. (Cut off the four corners by hand if no band saw is available.)
8. Carefully center the bottom of this blank on a face plate and fasten with suitable woodscrews.

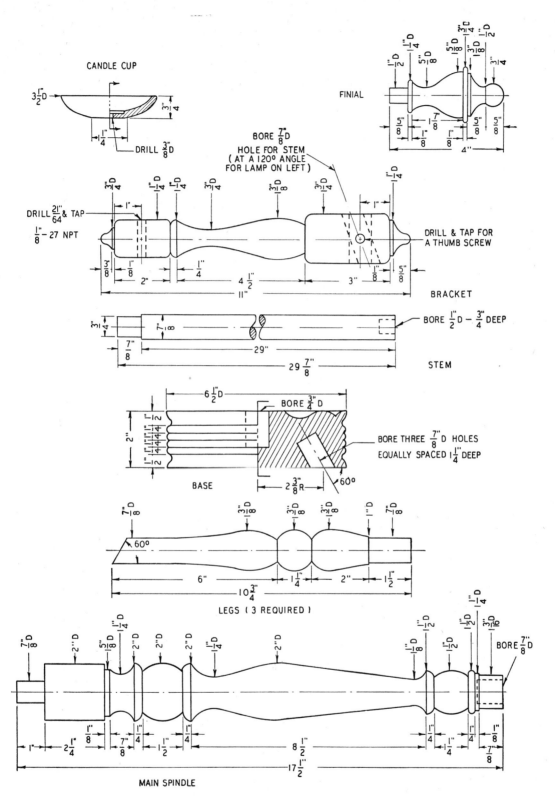

CANDLE CUP

$3\frac{1}{2}''$D

$\frac{3}{4}''$

$\frac{1}{4}''$

DRILL $\frac{3}{8}''$D

FINIAL

$\frac{1}{2}''$D

$\frac{1}{4}''$

$\frac{5}{8}''$D

$\frac{5}{8}''$D

$\frac{1}{4}''$

$\frac{3}{4}''$D

$\frac{3}{4}''$D

$\frac{1}{2}''$D

$\frac{3}{8}''$

$3\frac{1}{4}''$

$\frac{5}{8}''$

$1\frac{7}{8}''$

$\frac{1}{8}''$

$\frac{5}{8}''$

$\frac{5}{8}''$

$4''$

BORE $\frac{7}{8}''$D
HOLE FOR STEM
(AT A 120° ANGLE
FOR LAMP ON LEFT)

DRILL $\frac{21}{64}''$ & TAP

$\frac{1}{8}'' - 27$ NPT

$\frac{3}{4}''$D

$1''$

$\frac{1}{4}''$D

$\frac{3}{4}''$D

$3\frac{1}{8}''$

$3\frac{1}{4}''$D

$1\frac{1}{4}''$D

$1''$

DRILL & TAP FOR
A THUMB SCREW

$\frac{3}{8}''$

$\frac{1}{8}''$

$\frac{1}{4}''$

$4\frac{1}{2}''$

$3''$

$\frac{1}{8}''$

$\frac{5}{8}''$

$2''$

$11''$

BRACKET

$\frac{3}{4}''$

$\frac{7}{8}''$

BORE $\frac{1}{2}''$D $- \frac{3}{4}''$ DEEP

$\frac{7}{8}''$

$29''$

$29\frac{7}{8}''$

STEM

$6\frac{1}{2}''$D

BORE $\frac{3}{4}''$ D

$\frac{1}{2}''$

$\frac{1}{4}''$
$\frac{1}{4}''$
$\frac{1}{4}''$

$2''$

$\frac{1}{2}''$

BORE THREE $\frac{7}{8}''$ D HOLES
EQUALLY SPACED $1\frac{1}{4}''$ DEEP

BASE

$2\frac{3}{8}''$R

60°

$\frac{7}{8}''$D

60°

$3\frac{1}{8}''$D

$3\frac{1}{8}''$D

$3\frac{1}{8}''$D

$1''$D

$\frac{7}{8}''$D

$6''$

$1\frac{1}{4}''$

$2''$

$1\frac{1}{2}''$

$10\frac{3}{4}''$

LEGS (3 REQUIRED)

$\frac{7}{8}''$D

$2''$D

$\frac{5}{8}''$D

$1\frac{1}{4}''$D

$2''$D

$2''$D

$2''$D

$1\frac{1}{4}''$D

$2''$D

$1\frac{1}{8}''$D

$1\frac{1}{2}''$D

$1\frac{1}{2}''$D

$1\frac{1}{4}''$D

$3\frac{3}{16}''$D

BORE $\frac{7}{8}''$D

$1''$

$2\frac{1}{4}''$

$\frac{1}{8}''$

$\frac{7}{8}''$

$\frac{1}{4}''$

$1\frac{1}{2}''$

$\frac{1}{4}''$

$8\frac{1}{2}''$

$\frac{1}{4}''$

$1\frac{1}{4}''$

$\frac{1}{4}''$

$\frac{1}{8}''$

$\frac{7}{8}''$

$17\frac{1}{2}''$

MAIN SPINDLE

FIG. 6-16(a).

95

9. Turn the shape indicated and turn-bore the $\frac{3}{4}''$ D hole to receive the main spindle dowel.

10. Sand and apply a French polish. Do not sand or apply finish to $\frac{3}{4}''$ D hole.

11. Remove the base from the face plate.

Main Spindle:

1. Secure the stock for the main spindle and bore a $\frac{7}{8}''$ D hole in one end with an auger bit. This hole must line up exactly with the axis of the stock.

2. Prepare a wooden plug for this end by turning a short piece of stock in the lathe to a $\frac{7}{8}''$ diameter. Leave the dead center hole on the plug. This plug should be a snug fit in the hole.

3. Insert the plug in the hole, center the opposite end for a spur center, and mount the stock in the lathe between centers.

4. Turn to size as indicated. The $\frac{7}{8}''$ dowel end should fit snugly into the hole in the base piece.

5. Sand and apply a French polish to all surfaces except the dowel end.

6. Remove the main spindle from the lathe and pull out the plug.

Stem:

1. Center one end of the stem stock and drill and plug the opposite end in a manner similar to that described for the main spindle turning.

2. Turn the stem. It may be advisable to use a steady rest for this long, slender piece. See description of steady rest in Basic Operations.

3. Sand and apply French polish except for dowel end.

4. Remove stem from lathe and pull out the plug.

Bracket:

1. Center bracket stock and turn it to dimensions indicated.

2. Carefully locate and bore the hole for the stem as indicated.

3. Drill $\frac{21}{64}''$ D hole for the threaded socket nipple and tap this hole with a $\frac{1}{8}''$ pipe tap.

4. Bore a $\frac{7}{8}''$ D hole in the bracket to receive the stem.

5. Drill and tap the hole for a wooden or brass thumbscrew.

6. Sandpaper all surfaces and apply a French polish.

7. Cut off the waste on ends. Sand and apply several coats of shellac to these ends.

Candle Cup:

1. Glue up the candle-cup blank and face-plate block with a piece of heavy paper between them. Allow glue to dry.

2. Cut out the largest circle possible from this assembly.

3. Fasten the assembly to a small face plate and turn the candle cup to shape.

4. Sandpaper carefully and apply a French polish.

5. Bore a $\frac{3}{8}''$ hole as indicated and remove the cup from the chuck block with a chisel and mallet.

Finial:

1. Center stock for turning and turn the finial to dimensions between centers.

2. The ball on the end may be turned by chucking the dowel end of the turned finial in an outside chuck.

3. Sandpaper and apply a French polish.

Assembly:

1. Glue legs, base, main spindle and stem together with a suitable glue. Keep excess glue off finished surfaces by wiping with a clean, damp cloth.

2. Assemble socket and nipple to bracket. A $\frac{1}{8}''$ lock nut may be used to keep the socket from turning. Use a candle socket in the upright model.

3. Fit the bracket to the stem. If the bracket hole is too tight, sand the stem hole with coarse sandpaper wrapped tightly around a $\frac{3}{4}''$ dowel. Fasten the bracket in place with a wooden or brass thumbscrew.

4. Place finial in the hole at the top of the stem. It is not necessary to glue this in place.

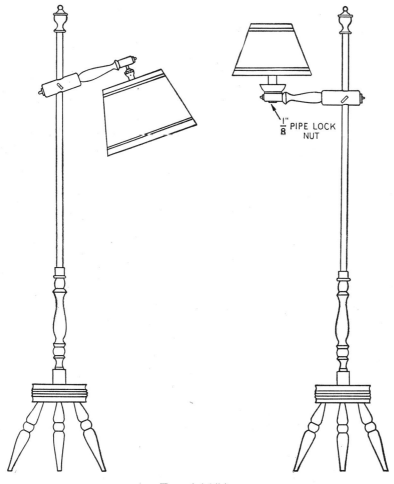

$\frac{1}{8}''$ PIPE LOCK NUT

FIG. 6-16(b).

17. SPIRAL LAMP

Spiral lamps are increasing in popularity. They may be made from practically any kind of wood, finished naturally, or in various colors. Keene's cement may also be used and is quite popular because of its weight and its color possibilities.

Materials Needed:

1 pc., 6″ × 6″ × 16″ solid mahogany

Procedure (see Fig. 6-17):

1. Turn a 16″ cylinder to a diameter of 6″.
2. Turn a section of this cylinder to a 4″ diameter, 12″ from one end. (See drawing.)
3. Lay out a double spiral on the 4″ × 12″ section of the cylinder. (See Basic Operations.)
4. Using a back saw, chisel, and wood rasp, form the spiral. (See Basic Operations.)
5. After sanding the lamp thoroughly, finish as desired. The lathe may be run at the lowest possible speed for sanding and French polishing.
6. Bore a $\frac{3}{8}$″ hole through the center of the lamp to accommodate the wire. This hole may be bored into the lamp from each end. Care should be taken to make the hole meet in the center. A 1″ hole may be counterbored in the bottom (as indicated on the drawing) to facilitate wiring. Another $\frac{21}{64}$″ hole may be bored through the base to meet the center hole (see drawing). Tap the hole with a $\frac{1}{8}$″ pipe tap. A $\frac{3}{8}$″ bakelite bushing may be screwed into the end of the hole in the base. These bushings may be obtained when the craftsman purchases the lamp sockets and other fittings. It is necessary to tap the top end of the $\frac{3}{8}$″ hole to receive a $\frac{1}{8}$″ pipe nipple. The socket will then be mounted on this nipple.

The craftsman may wish to make the lamp from two pieces of stock glued together. A groove may be made through the center of each piece, before gluing them together, and thus the hole for the wire will be made in advance of the turning. The ends of the hole may be plugged with two small pieces of tapered wood for centering.

7. The craftsman may also wish to have a square base on the lamp instead of a cylindrical one. (See detail and Basic Operations.)

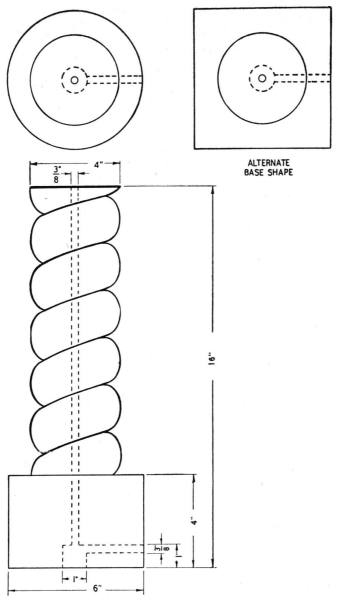

ALTERNATE
BASE SHAPE

FIG. 6-17.

18. PLASTIC CANDLESTICK

The candlestick illustrated in Fig. 6-18 was turned on a home workshop wood lathe. The material used was clear Plexiglas. Most of the plastics may be easily turned by using the scraping method of wood turning. Take light cuts with sharp tools to avoid heating and consequent discoloration.

Materials Needed:

1 pc., base stock:	$\frac{7}{8}'' \times 4\frac{1}{4}'' \times 4\frac{1}{4}''$	Plexiglas or Lucite
1 pc., stem stock:	$1''$ dia. $\times 6''$	Plexiglas or Lucite
1 pc., chuck piece for stem:	$1'' \times 3''$ dia.	hardwood
1 pc., face-plate block for base:	$\frac{3}{4}'' \times 4'' \times 4''$	hardwood
1 plug	$\frac{3}{4}''$ dia. $\times 1\frac{1}{2}''$	birch dowel

Procedure (see Fig. 6-18):

1. Drill a $\frac{3}{4}''$ hole in one end of the plastic rod to a depth of about $\frac{5}{8}''$. This hole will serve to hold a wooden plug (or chuck) while the stem is being turned and later will be the hole to receive the base of the candle.

2. Cut off a $1\frac{1}{2}''$ length of $\frac{3}{4}''$ dowel and force it into the $\frac{3}{4}''$ hole in the plastic rod. Shim with paper if necessary, to provide a snug fit.

3. Mount the chuck piece for the stem on the face plate and turn a snug fitting hole for the dowel on the bottom end of the plastic rod. (See Fig. 6-18(a).)

4. Mount the $6''$ plastic rod as shown in Fig. 6-18(a) and turn the stem according to dimensions shown. The end which is to be cemented into the base is cut almost off with the parting tool and then sawed off by hand after the stem is turned and polished.

5. Polish with emery cloth, remove from the chucks, and buff with standard plastic abrasives.

6. Prepare the face-plate block for turning the base. The faces of this block should be smooth and parallel.

7. Apply a priming coat and a second coat of "Duco" cement, to one face of the wood block. Apply a coat of cement to one face of the plastic base stock. Insert a piece of heavy paper between these surfaces and clamp them together until the cement sets.

8. Lay out and saw a $4\frac{1}{8}''$ disk from the two cemented blocks.

9. Mount the face-plate block on the face plate with $\frac{3}{4}''$ No. 10 flathead screws.

10. Turn the base to dimensions shown. Be sure that the hole for the stem is a good fit and that the stem does not quite touch bottom in the hole.

11. Polish with emery cloth.

12. Remove the face plate from the lathe and disengage the plastic base from the face-plate block. This is done by inserting a chisel point into the paper separator with the bevel toward the wood and hitting the chisel a sharp blow.

13. Remove any excess paper from the base and then buff to a high luster. Cement on a slightly oversized piece of felt. Then trim the felt to the required size with a razor blade.

14. Cement the stem to base with Plexiglas cement.

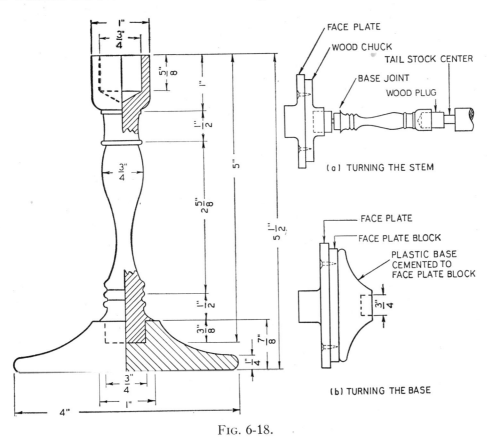

FIG. 6-18.

19. SPUN LAMP BASE

The lamp base shown in Fig. 6-19 is typical of the many practical articles which may be made by the spinning process utilizing the wood lathe. The one shown was spun from 22-gauge copper. Pewter, aluminum, and silver may also be easily spun.

Materials Needed:

2 pc., wooden disks: 2″ thick 6″ dia., pine or bass
2 pc., metal disks: 22 gauge 6″ dia., annealed copper
1 socket support: $\frac{1}{8}$″ threaded pipe about 6″ long, brass
1 socket: $\frac{1}{8}$″ base, brass or nickel
1 length of wire: No. 14 parallel-pair 8-ft., plastic

Procedure (see Fig. 6-19):

1. Attach a disk of wood to a face plate and turn the bottom form to the shape shown in Fig. 6-19(a). Leave this form on the face plate and do not remove the face plate from the spindle until the bottom half of the lamp base has been spun. This will insure a true running form.

2. Review the spinning procedure outlined in Basic Operations and spin one of the 6″ copper disks over the form just made. If copper is being used, be sure to anneal repeatedly as the disk is formed to its new shape. Usually annealing will be necessary each time the copper is pushed in toward the form approximately $\frac{1}{2}$″. Trim off the excess edge so that the bottom piece is 5″ in diameter. Polish before removing from the form.

3. Turn the top form as shown in Fig. 6-19(b). The $\frac{1}{4}$″ rim on the form will be utilized to spin the burr that will hold the two copper lamp pieces together. Note that the rim diameter of this form must be slightly greater than the maximum diameter of the bottom form.

4. Spin the second copper disk and trim off the edge so as to allow for a $\frac{3}{16}$″ burr. Anneal again and then turn the burr over so that it will fit the form snugly. Polish before removing from the form.

5. Bore the holes to receive the $\frac{1}{8}$″ pipe.

6. Snap the two pieces together. If difficulty is encountered, file a little off the edge of the bottom piece. Install the $\frac{1}{8}$″ pipe in place; attach and wire the socket.

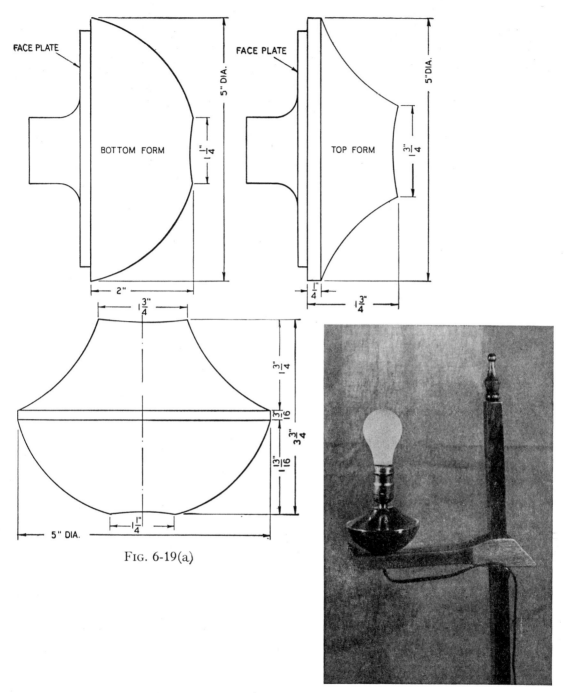

FACE PLATE

BOTTOM FORM

5" DIA.

$1\frac{1}{4}$"

2"

FACE PLATE

TOP FORM

5" DIA.

$1\frac{3}{4}$"

$\frac{1}{4}$"

$1\frac{3}{4}$"

$1\frac{3}{4}$"

$1\frac{3}{4}$"

$\frac{3}{16}$"

$3\frac{3}{4}$"

$1\frac{3}{16}$"

$1\frac{1}{4}$"

5" DIA.

FIG. 6-19(a)

FIG. 6-19(b).

20. KEENE'S CEMENT TURNED BOX WITH LID

The box shown in the accompanying photographs was made from Keene's cement and is a face plate project. The craftsman will want to vary the dimensions according to the use of the box. Such projects as cigarette boxes, jewel boxes, powder boxes, and candy boxes are very popular.

Materials Needed:

1 pc., 6″ × 6″ Keene's cement block. (See Basic Operations for mixing and mounting Keene's cement for turning.)

Procedure (see Figs. 6-20a-e):

1. Mount the block of Keene's cement on the headstock of the lathe and true up the cylinder. The lid and box will be turned from one piece.

2. Turn the *inside* of the lid first. (See Fig. 6-20a.) Cut a rabbet on the *outside* edge of the lid. The rabbet may also be cut on the inside edge. (See sketch, Fig. 6-20b.)

3. Using a parting tool, cut off the lid from the cement block. Care must be taken to catch the lid so it will not drop and break. (See Fig. 6-20a.) The lathe should be revolving at the slowest possible speed. The lid may be sawed off the block if the craftsman desires to do so.

4. Turn the deep recess of the box to dimensions. (See Figs. 6-20c and 6-20e.)

5. Make a rabbet on the *inside* edge of the box to receive the lid. Frequent checks should be made when turning the rabbet on this portion of the box as the lid must be a tight press fit.

6. Press the lid onto the box. The outside shape of the lid and the outside shape of the box may now be turned together. This insures a perfect match of the two pieces. (See Fig. 6-20d.)

7. Finish as desired. The tight fit of the lid can be relieved by lightly sanding the rabbet on the box.

FIG. 6-20(a).

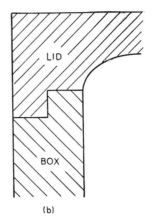

LID

BOX

(b)

FIG. 6-20(b).

(c)

FIG. 6-20(c).

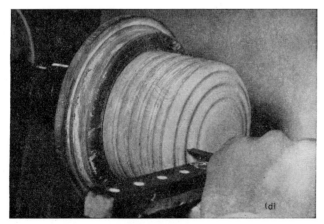

(d)

FIG. 6-20(d)

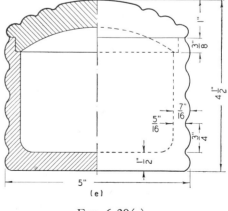

(e)

FIG. 6-20(e).

21. FLOOR LAMP

This floor lamp is a project that contains excellent turning exercises plus other bits of unusual woodworking. It can be made of maple, mahogany, walnut, gum, cherry, oak, or any other wood that turns well. The lamp in the picture having three bulbs could be changed into a three-way variety if so desired.

Materials Needed:

4 pc., (A) legs:	$2'' \times 2'' \times 10\frac{1}{2}''$	maple
1 pc., (B) base:	$2'' \times 9\frac{1}{4}'' \times 9\frac{1}{4}''$	maple
1 pc., (C) center standard:	$3\frac{1}{2}'' \times 3\frac{1}{2}'' \times 13\frac{1}{2}''$	maple
1 pc., (D) table & column support:	$1\frac{1}{2}'' \times 4'' \times 13\frac{5}{8}''$	maple
1 pc., (E) table:	$1\frac{1}{8}'' \times 8\frac{1}{4}'' \times 12\frac{5}{8}''$	maple
1 pc., (F) column:	$2'' \times 2'' \times 22''$	maple
1 pc., (G) light rest:	$1\frac{1}{2}'' \times 6'' \times 6''$	maple
1 pc., (H) upper column:	$1\frac{1}{4}'' \times 1\frac{1}{4}'' \times 8\frac{1}{2}''$	maple
1 pc., (I) finial:	$1'' \times 1'' \times 3\frac{1}{2}''$	maple

1 metal piece to cover the channel
3 sockets
1 toggle switch
1 plug
wire

Procedure (see Fig. 6-21):

A. *Legs*

1. Set the pieces for the legs in a lathe on centers and turn to the required shape. It is well to have the dowel end of the legs on the tailstock end so that the size can be tested after a small portion has been turned.
2. Sand and apply one coat of shellac.

B. *Base Piece*

1. This is a piece which is partly turned, then finished with the band saw, sand disk, and shaper.
2. Be sure that the piece has a smooth and flat side which is placed against the face plate when setting this up for turning.
3. Set the piece up on the face plate and turn the contour on the top of the piece.
4. The hole should be turn-bored while the piece is on the face plate, and tested for size.
5. The corners can be shaped on the band saw.
6. All edges can be smoothed on the sand disk.
7. Cut the molded edge on the shaper.
8. Lay out the holes for the legs. A template or jig may be used as a guide while boring the holes.
9. Bore the holes about $1\frac{1}{2}''$ deep.

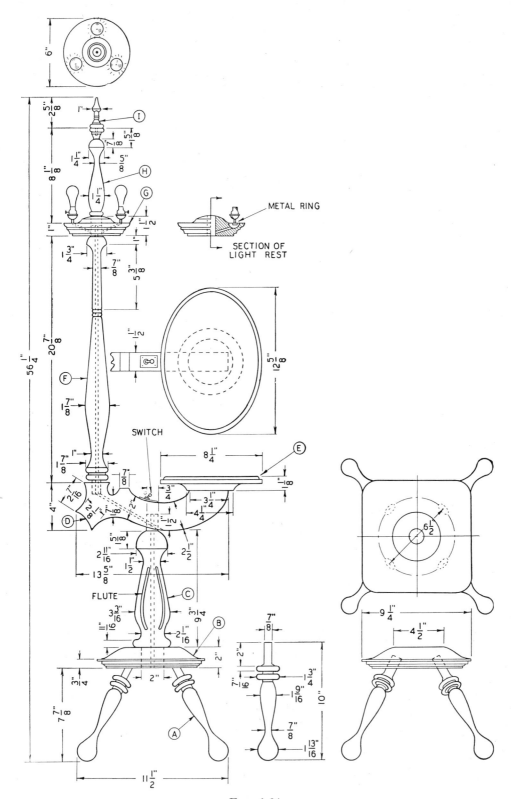

METAL RING

SECTION OF
LIGHT REST

SWITCH

FLUTE

FIG. 6-21.

107

C. *Center Standard*

1. Set this piece up on the lathe on centers and turn as indicated in the drawing. You will note it has a dowel on both ends.

2. The large dowel end should be on the headstock end because this is large enough to allow turning outside of the live center.

3. The fluting may be done while the column is in the lathe as per basic operations.

4. Bore the $\frac{3}{8}''$ hole for the wire.

D. *Table and Column Support*

1. This piece can be sawed out on the band saw and finished with a file and sandpaper.

2. The flat where the tray sits should be carefully planed at right angles to the work face.

3. The hole to receive the column should be carefully bored so that this will be perpendicular to the flat surface just planed.

4. The hole for the center standard dowel is bored parallel to the hole just bored.

5. Bore the holes for the wire as per drawing. (Note how this must be recessed to enable the wire to enter center standard.)

6. Make the recess for the toggle switch.

E. *Table*

1. This piece is mounted with the top side toward the face plate by the paper, glue, sandwich method.

2. Turn the bottom as per drawing. Sand.

3. Remove from face plate piece and band saw to shape.

4. Smooth the edge on the sand disk.

5. Make molded edge on the shaper.

6. Give one coat of shellac.

F. *Column*

1. Set this piece up on centers and turn as indicated on the drawing.

2. You will notice there is a dowel on either end of the piece. Usually, the smaller of the two is the one that is placed toward the tailstock.

3. Bore the hole for the wire by use of the lathe, and bore from both ends of the piece.

4. Sand and shellac.

G. *Light Rest*

1. Turn the piece which supports the three bulbs. This is turned on a face plate and the dowel hole turn-bored while it is mounted on the plate.

2. You will notice that the dowel hole can be turned from the front side because it can go all the way through.

3. Also note that the circular channel which is recessed for wiring is covered with a metal ring which holds the socket nipples.

H. *Upper Column*

1. Mount this piece in the lathe on centers and turn as per drawing. Care should be used when turning the dowel to size.
2. Bore the hole in the top end to receive the finial.
3. Sand and shellac.

I. *Finial*

1. This is a piece that can be turned by protruding from a chuck.
2. If a chuck is not available, it should be turned between centers with the top end toward the tailstock turned down to as small a diameter as practical.
3. It can then be finished by hand after the final dead center support has been cut off.

Assembly:

After all parts have been made, it would be well to assemble the project to be sure that sizes are correct (without driving the dowels in all the way). It is good practice to wedge the dowels of the main supporting pieces. When wedging, be sure that the slot for the wedge is placed at right angles to the direction of the grain. Before assembling, be sure that the holes for the wire are continuous through the pieces so that the wire may be carried up through to the top of the lamp. Glue and assemble all parts, except the finial. Allow the glue to dry twenty-four hours then scrape off all excess and sand for finishing. Plenty of time should be used when sanding for finishing because it must be sanded parallel to the grain to avoid scratching. Finish as desired. Do the electric wiring and install the switch, sockets, and plug.

22. END TABLE

This end table may be made from practically any kind of cabinetwood. Birch and maple are ideal. The dimensions may be changed and the table may be finished according to taste. A light wood, finished natural, is very popular.

Materials Needed:

2 pc., leg end blocks:	$2\frac{1}{2}'' \times 2\frac{1}{2}'' \times 2\frac{1}{2}''$	maple
1 pc., top:	$1\frac{1}{2}'' \times 24'' \times 36''$	maple
4 pc., upper legs:	$2'' \times 2'' \times 11\frac{3}{4}''$	maple
4 pc., lower legs:	$2'' \times 2'' \times 12\frac{3}{4}''$	maple
1 pc., stretcher:	$2'' \times 2'' \times 25\frac{1}{4}''$	maple
2 pc., plugs:	$1'' \times 1'' \times 2''$	maple

Procedure (see Fig. 6-22):

1. Glue-up stock for top.
2. Square top.
3. Turn upper four sections of legs. A $\frac{3}{4}'' \times 1\frac{3}{8}''$ dowel should be turned on the small end of each section and a $\frac{3}{4}'' \times \frac{7}{8}''$ dowel on the large end.
4. Turn lower four sections of legs. A $\frac{3}{4}'' \times \frac{7}{8}''$ dowel should be turned on the large end of each section.
5. Square blocks to $2\frac{1}{2}'' \times 2\frac{1}{2}'' \times 2\frac{1}{2}''$.
6. Prick-punch the center of four adjacent sides of each block and bore the holes for the $\frac{3}{4}'' \times \frac{7}{8}''$ dowels.
7. Turn stretcher to dimension with a $\frac{3}{4}'' \times \frac{7}{8}''$ dowel at each end.
8. Bore holes in both blocks to accommodate dowels.
9. Lay out position of holes for legs in underside of top.
10. Bore holes for dowels. The holes should be bored at an angle of 45°.
11. Assemble, glue, and clamp under bracing.
12. Fasten under bracing to top by gluing dowels into holes.
13. Trim leg bottoms parallel to floor.
14. Finish as desired.

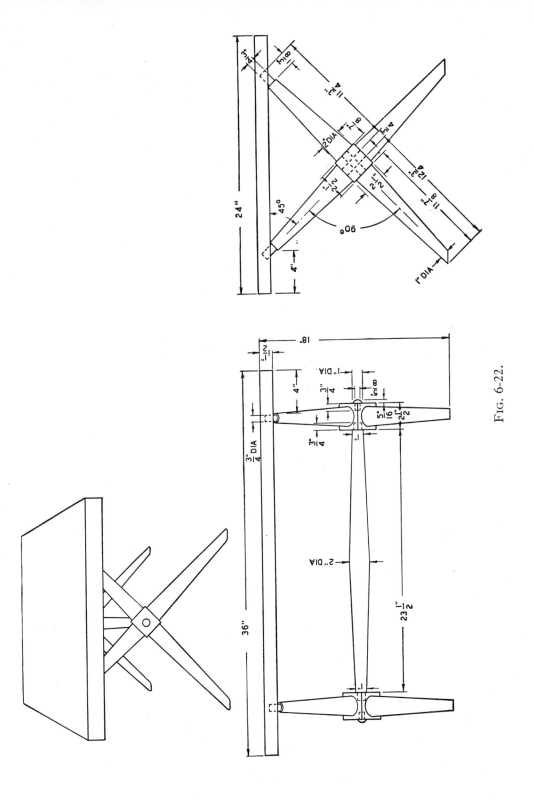

Fig. 6-22.

111

23. LAZY SUSAN

This project, very useful in the home, is an advanced project in wood-turning. The details as indicated in the drawing can be changed to other designs, but the design shown is typical and is made after a pattern which has been successful in use. Mahogany, walnut, red gum, oak, maple, or any other firm, well-seasoned wood can be used. It is usually finished in a natural color. It is a piece that should not be painted since it will be in contact with food. It may be finished similar to the dining room furniture.

Materials Needed:

1 pc., base: 8″ square, 3″ thick
1 pc., top: 16″ square, 3″ thick
1 round-head stove bolt, $\frac{1}{4} \times 3''$
1 wooden or metal spacer-bushing
1 brass plate

Procedure (see Fig. 6-23):

Base

1. Prepare the base for turning and fasten to the face plate as indicated in Basic Operations. The turning should be roughed out with a round-nosed tool.
2. The bearing should be carefully measured and fitted in the turned hole in the base. Any standard automobile bearing or roller-skate wheel can be used which has a race on the outside and inside and can be fitted by pushing into the turned hole as shown on the drawing.
3. After the base has been roughly turned to shape, smooth up carefully with a round-nosed tool and sand to a smooth surface. A priming coat of shellac should be applied to this surface before removing from the face plate.

Top

1. Mount the piece on the face plate and turn the top surface first.
2. Turn the underside as far as possible.
3. Set the piece up in an outside friction wooden chuck. (See Basic Operations.)
4. Turn the remaining sections of the underside and make the recess for the head of the supporting bolt.
5. Sand smooth.
6. Prime coat with shellac.
7. Fasten stove bolt to top pieces with brass plate and screws.

Assembly:

1. Push bearings and spacers into the bottom piece.
2. Inspect, rub down, and put on final finish.
3. When finish is dry, insert shaft into bearings. Be sure to put in spacer washers. The project is now complete.

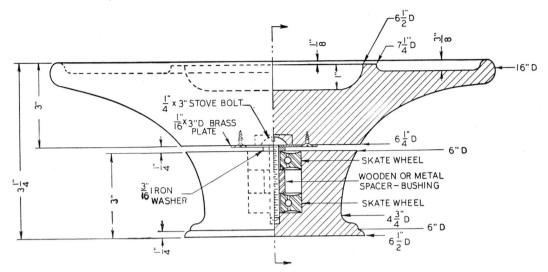

$6\frac{1}{2}"$ D

$7\frac{1}{4}"$ D

$\frac{1}{8}"$

$\frac{3}{8}"$

16" D

$\frac{1}{8}"$

3"

$\frac{1}{4}" \times 3"$ STOVE BOLT

$\frac{1}{16}" \times 3"$ D BRASS PLATE

$3\frac{1}{4}"$

3"

$\frac{1}{4}"$

$\frac{3}{16}"$ IRON WASHER

$\frac{1}{4}"$

$6\frac{1}{4}"$ D

6" D

SKATE WHEEL

WOODEN OR METAL SPACER – BUSHING

SKATE WHEEL

$4\frac{3}{4}"$ D

6" D

$6\frac{1}{2}"$ D

FIG. 6-23(a).

FIG. 6-23(b).

113

24. TURNED PICTURE FRAMES

Picture frames, whether large or small, can be turned on a lathe if a circular frame is the type wanted. Small frames are turned on a chuck as described in Basic Operations, and can be made from almost any type of wood—soft wood if the frame is to be painted, cabinet wood if the natural finish is desired. The project about to be described is a frame 18″ in diameter with a cross section of $\frac{3}{4}$″ × 2″. The wood suggested is black walnut, and it is a frame built up out of segments, sometimes called felloes.

Materials Needed:

12 pc., segments:	$\frac{3}{4}$″ × $4\frac{1}{2}$″ × 10″	black walnut
2 pc., arms:	2″ × 4″ × 24″	pine
4 pc., blocks:	1″ × 3″ × 4″	pine

Procedure (see Fig. 6-24):

1. This frame can be made by laying out a pattern of a full-sized circle of both inside and outside diameters.

2. Cut out a section of this circle for a pattern equal to at least $\frac{1}{6}$ of the circumference.

3. Cut this pattern exactly to the finished size and shape.

4. Lay this on the wood to be used, with the grain parallel to the longest dimension of the pattern. The segments should be laid out exactly according to the outline of the pattern. Allowance is made for finishing by allowing about $\frac{1}{16}$″ beyond layout to give extra material.

5. Saw out 12 sections.

6. Fit the ends of these pieces carefully to form two complete rings.

7. Assemble with glue and screws as per drawings.

8. Make a cross lap support frame of the 2 × 4's.

9. Lay out an $18\frac{1}{2}$″ circle on this frame.

10. Center carefully and screw to the outboard face plate.

11. Drill screw hole for mounting the assembled frame stock.

12. Mount assembled stock on this cross lap support.

13. Put on lathe and turn the front face and outer and inner edge of the picture frame.

14. Sand carefully and give a French polish.

15. Remove from cross lap support.

16. Fasten securely the four blocks on the cross lap support on the circumference of a $17\frac{3}{4}$″ circle.

17. Put cross lap support on outboard spindle and turn inside of blocks to form an outside chuck for the picture frame.

18. Face the arms of the cross lap chuck to insure that it will run true.

19. Mount frame in chuck with the front on the faced surface of the cross lap arms.

20. Turn the rabbet and face the back.

21. Give a priming coat of shellac.

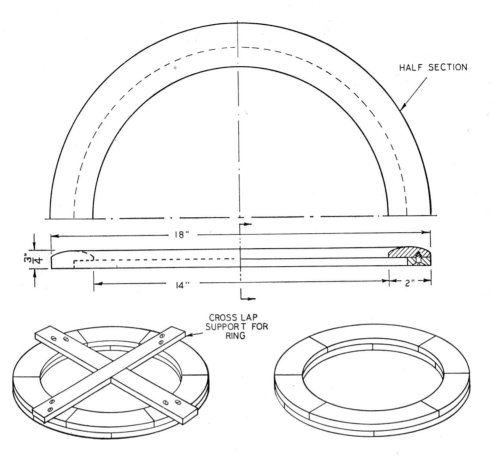

HALF SECTION

18"

3"/4

14"

2"

CROSS LAP
SUPPORT FOR
RING

ALTERNATE FRAME SHAPES

FIG. 6-24.

25. SCALLOPED CANDY DISH

This dish makes an interesting face-plate project. The scalloped edge may be designed by the craftsman to add a little personal touch.

Materials Needed:

1 pc., dish:	$2'' \times 7'' \times 7''$	walnut
1 pc., face-plate block:	$\frac{3}{4}'' \times 6'' \times 6''$	white pine

Procedure (see Fig. 6-25):

1. Surface the piece of white pine to be used as the face-plate block.
2. Surface one face of the piece of walnut for the dish.
3. Locate the center of each piece and scribe a circle with a 6″ diameter on the piece of pine and $6\frac{5}{8}''$ circle on the piece of walnut.
4. Cut out both pieces of stock just outside of the scribed circles.
5. With a piece of heavy wrapping paper inserted between the two pieces, glue the trued-up surface of the walnut stock to the piece of pine.
6. Fasten the pine piece to a face-plate with $\frac{3}{4}''$ No. 12 flathead screws.
7. Turn the candy dish to the required size and shape.
8. Sand thoroughly and apply a French polish while the work is mounted on the lathe.
9. Remove the face plate. Insert a chisel on the paper line between the pine face-plate block and the finished dish. Rap the chisel handle sharply to remove the pine piece.
10. Sand the bottom of the dish.
11. Lay out the design for the scalloped edge using a stiff paper pattern.
12. Using a coping saw, cut out the scalloped edge.
13. Sand carefully and apply a finish to match the finish applied on the lathe.

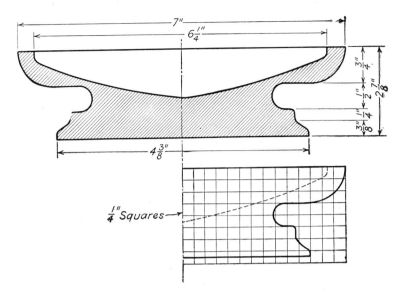

Fig. 6-25(a).

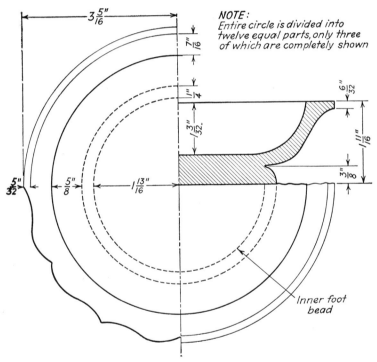

NOTE:
Entire circle is divided into
twelve equal parts, only three
of which are completely shown

Inner foot
bead

Fig. 6-25(b).

A   B

Fig. 6-25(c).

26. CHEESE AND CRACKER TRAY

This tray and bowl is a very interesting project to be made by face-plate turning. The tray is made on the outboard face plate. A recess is made in the center of the tray to accommodate the bowl. The bowl may be removed and replaced with the round tile on which cheese may be sliced.

The tray and bowl shown were made of cherry wood, but any close-grained hardwood such as maple or birch would be equally attractive.

Materials Needed:

4 pcs., tray sections: 2″ × 7″ × 14″ or 1 pc., 2″ × 7″ × 36″ cherry
8 pcs., bowl sections: 1″ × 4″ × 6″ or 1 pc., 2″ × 7″ × 36″ cherry
1—6″ D porcelain tile

Procedure (see Fig. 6-26):

Tray

1. Cut each piece into a segment as shown in Fig. A or in Fig. B.
2. Glue the four segments together so that the grain pattern is formed as shown in the working drawing and picture. This method of gluing the segments will produce a circular tray which will not show any end grain.
3. Plane one surface of the glued-up stock true and flat.
4. Locate the center at the intersection of the four segments and scribe a circle of the required diameter.
5. Using a band saw or a hand turning saw, cut out the circle.
6. Fasten an outboard face plate to the surfaced side of the stock, using screws.
7. Mount the piece on the outboard spindle and turn to required shape. (*Caution*) Be sure that the tool rest is properly adjusted so that there is sufficient clearance. Turn at slow speed.
8. Sand thoroughly and finish as desired. If cherry is used, a natural French polish gives a very nice finish to this project.

Bowl

9. Cut the eight pieces into segments as was done for the tray.
10. Glue up the segments to make two sections for the bowl.
11. Plane a smooth flat surface on each glued-up section and glue the two surfaces together so that the glue joint on the bottom section is located in the center of a segment in the top section (Fig. C).
12. Plane one surface smooth and flat.
13. At the intersection of the segments, locate the center of the piece of stock and scribe a circle to the finished diameter.
14. Cut the circle just outside the scribed line.
15. Mount on a face plate and turn to the required size and shape. Make sure the base of the bowl is the correct size to fit into the recess in the center of the tray.
16. Sand and finish to match the tray.
17. Obtain a colorful circular tile to fit into the recess in the tray.

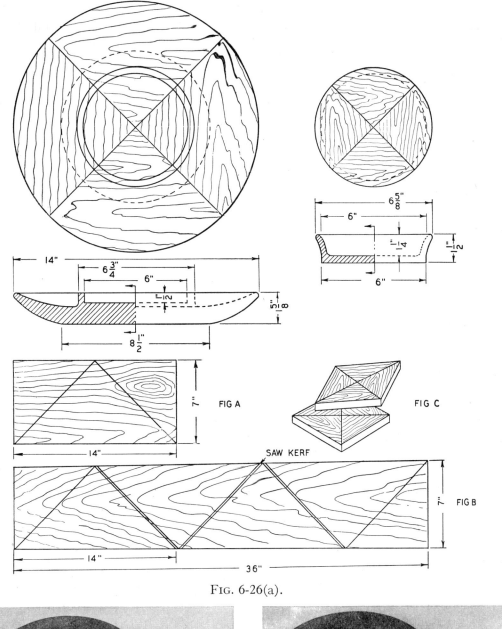

14"

6¾"

6"

½"

5⅛"

8½"

6⅝"

6"

¼"

½"

6"

7"

FIG A

14"

FIG C

SAW KERF

7"

FIG B

14"

36"

FIG. 6-26(a).

FIG. 6-26(b).

FIG. 6-26(c).

27. TILT-TOP TABLE

A tilt-top table is a useful and a decorative piece of furniture. It can be tucked back in a corner with the top tilted, or it can be used as a lamp table or side table with the top in a horizontal position.

Materials Needed:

1 pc., center post:	$3\frac{1}{2}'' \times 3\frac{1}{2}'' \times 25''$	walnut or mahogany
3 pc., legs:	$1'' \times 4'' \times 14''$	walnut or mahogany
1 pc., top:	$1'' \times 16'' \times 22''$	walnut or mahogany
2 pcs., top cleats:	$1'' \times 1\frac{1}{4}'' \times 14''$	walnut or mahogany
1 pc., top block:	$1\frac{1}{4}'' \times 4'' \times 4\frac{1}{2}''$	walnut or mahogany
1 pc., cold rolled steel:	$\frac{1}{4}'' \times 5''$	
6 dowels:	$\frac{3}{8}'' \times 1\frac{1}{2}''$	birch

Procedure (see Fig. 6-27):

1. Mount the center post between centers and turn to required dimensions.
2. Sand thoroughly.
3. Divide the circumference of the section for fastening the feet into three equal parts.
4. Lay out the holes for the dowels to fasten the feet. Bore $\frac{3}{8}''$ holes, $\frac{3}{4}''$ deep.
5. Surface the stock for the legs to required dimensions.
6. Make a pattern of the shape of the legs. Use cardboard for the pattern.
7. Lay out the pattern on the stock so that the grain runs parallel to the length.
8. Cut out the legs with a band saw, jig saw, or coping saw and smooth to the lines.
9. Lay out the holes for the dowels in the legs. Be sure these holes line up with the holes in the post.
10. Bore the $\frac{3}{8}''$ holes, $\frac{3}{4}''$ deep.
11. Place the dowels in the holes and test for fit. While the legs are in position, mark off the thickness of the legs on the post.
12. With a chisel, flatten off the area to allow the leg to fit snugly to the post.
13. Glue and clamp the legs to the post. It is advisable to glue one leg at a time.
14. Cut and shape the top cleats to size.
15. Cut and shape the top block to size.
16. Locate the center of the top block and bore a $1\frac{1}{4}''$ hole, $1''$ deep. This should fit snugly on the tenon at the top of the post.
17. In the center of the rounded corner of the top block, bore a $\frac{1}{4}''$ hole through the piece.
18. In the center of the top block, bore a hole and countersink for a $1''$ No. 12 flathead screw.

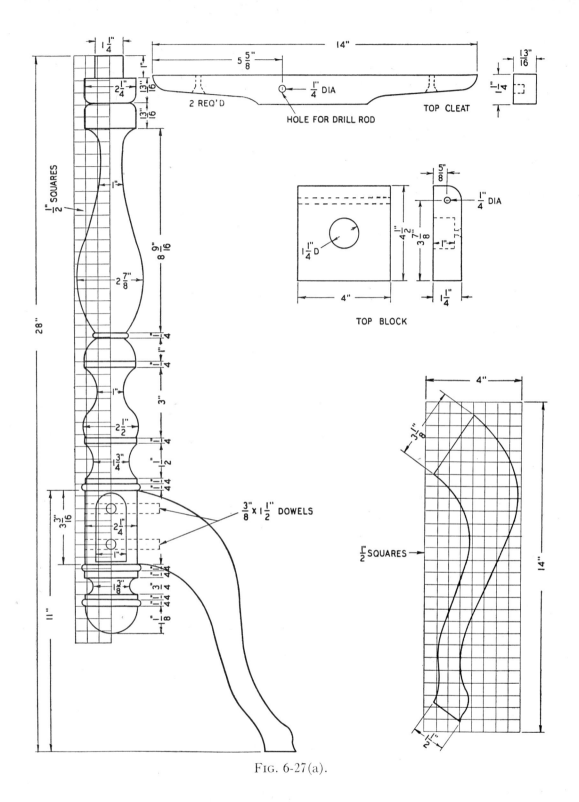

Labels visible in the drawing:

$1\frac{1}{4}''$

$2\frac{1}{4}''$

$\frac{13}{16}''$

$\frac{13}{16}''$

$1''$

$\frac{1}{2}''$ SQUARES

$28''$

$1''$

$8\frac{9}{16}''$

$2\frac{7}{8}''$

$1\frac{1}{4}''$

$3''$

$2\frac{1}{2}''$

$1\frac{3}{4}''$

$3\frac{3}{16}''$

$2\frac{1}{4}''$

$1''$

$11''$

$1\frac{3}{8}''$

$\frac{3}{8}'' \times 1\frac{1}{2}''$ DOWELS

$14''$

$5\frac{5}{8}''$

$\frac{1}{4}''$ DIA

2 REQ'D

HOLE FOR DRILL ROD

TOP CLEAT

$\frac{13}{16}''$

$1\frac{1}{4}''$

$\frac{5}{8}''$

$\frac{1}{4}''$ DIA

$4\frac{1}{2}''$

$3\frac{7}{8}''$

$1''$

$1\frac{1}{4}''$ D

$4''$

$1\frac{1}{4}''$

TOP BLOCK

$4''$

$3\frac{1}{8}''$

$\frac{1}{2}''$ SQUARES

$14''$

$2\frac{7}{8}''$

FIG. 6-27(a).

19. Place the top block on a flat surface with the rounded corner down. Push a piece of $\frac{1}{4}''$ steel rod through the hole so that $\frac{1}{4}''$ projects from each side. Lay the top cleats on each side of the top block so that they are evenly centered. Press the top cleats against the ends of the rod to locate the position of the holes.

20. Bore a $\frac{1}{4}''$ hole, $\frac{1}{2}''$ deep in the top cleats.

21. Square up the piece for the top to required dimensions.

22. Make a full-size pattern of the shape of the top.

23. Lay out the design for the top and cut to the line.

24. Smooth the edges just cut.

25. With a spindle shaper or with a hand gouge shape the molded edge.

26. Sand all parts thoroughly.

27. Assemble the top block, top cleats and the top. This is done by fastening the top cleats to the under part of the top with screws.

28. Fasten the top assembly to the post with glue and a screw.

29. Sand thoroughly and finish as desired.

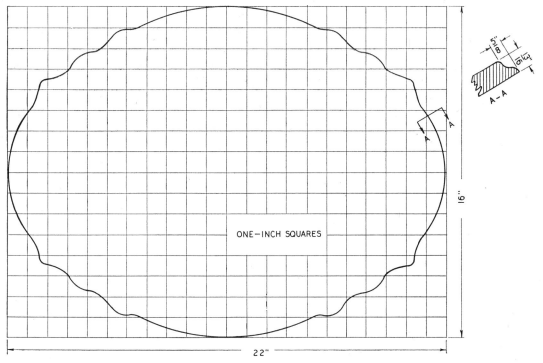

ONE-INCH SQUARES

16"

22"

A–A

FIG. 6-27(b).

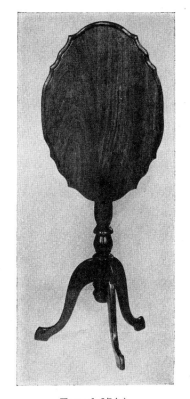

FIG. 6-27(c).

FIG. 6-27(d).

FIG. 6-27(e).

28. KEENE'S CEMENT TABLE LAMP

A table lamp made of Keene's cement can be easily made on the wood-turning lathe. Variation in color can be obtained to suit the craftsman's desires. The craftsman does not get the same "feel" of working with this material as he does while working with wood, but the operations are similar and the results are gratifying.

Materials Needed:

1 pc., base mold:	$2'' \times 6'' \times 6''$	white pine
1 pc., threaded $\frac{1}{8}''$ pipe:	$12\frac{1}{2}''$	brass
2—$\frac{1}{8}''$ brass lock nuts to fit pipe		
1 pc., galvanized iron	18 gauge $12'' \times 19''$	

Procedure (see Fig. 6-28):

1. Mount the piece of white pine on a face plate and turn to the required dimensions as shown in Fig. A. This piece is to be used for the base of the mold. (See Basic Operations.)

2. Bore a $\frac{3}{8}''$ hole in the center of the master base $\frac{1}{4}''$ to $\frac{3}{8}''$ deep to accommodate the $\frac{1}{8}''$ brass pipe.

3. Fasten the piece of sheet metal around the master base piece (Fig. B).

4. With a hack saw, notch one end of the pipe as shown (Fig. C).

5. Place the brass pipe in the hole of the base with the notched end up. Temporarily plug the hole of the upper end of the pipe.

6. Mix the Keene's cement and pour into the mold. Allow to harden for about 18 hours.

7. Remove the sheet metal form and the wooden base.

8. Screw a lock nut on each end of the pipe and turn them to fit snugly against the cement.

9. Mount the block of Keene's cement on the lathe between centers. Use a 60° center for the dead center rather than a cup center. Fit the spurs of the live center into notches in the threaded pipe. If the work has a tendency to vibrate on the live center, the end of the pipe may be plugged with hardwood into which the point of the live center may be pressed. As an alternate method, if a drill chuck is available, it may be used to hold the live center end of the pipe.

10. Running the lathe at a slow speed, turn the lamp to size and shape as required.

11. Allow to dry for several days, then sand with very fine wet-dry sandpaper. See Basic Operations for polishing the lamp.

12. Remove the top lock nut and cut off the threaded pipe allowing $\frac{3}{8}''$ to project from the end of the lamp.

13. Drill a $\frac{3}{8}''$ hole into the base as indicated in the drawing.

14. Wire the lamp.

    Caution: Protect any surface on which the lamp will be placed from the moisture in the lamp base. Keene's cement dries slowly.

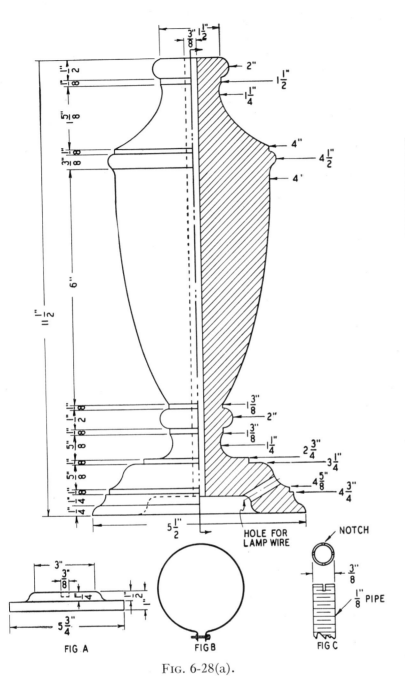

FIG A

FIG B

FIG C

NOTCH

HOLE FOR
LAMP WIRE

Fig. 6-28(a).

Fig. 6-28(b).

29. COLONIAL TABLE LAMP

Many people are partial to furniture of colonial design. The lamp described here should satisfy the desire for colonial design and provide some interesting turning experience.

Materials Needed:

1 pc., lamp standard:	$4\frac{3}{4}'' \times 4\frac{3}{4}'' \times 12''$	maple
3 pcs., legs:	$1\frac{3}{4}'' \times 1\frac{3}{4}'' \times 10''$	maple

Procedure (see Fig. 6-29):

1. Prepare the stock for turning the standard. This may be done in either of the following ways:

    (a) Obtain a solid piece of maple $4\frac{3}{4}''$ square by $12''$ long, or

    (b) Obtain two pieces $2\frac{3}{8}'' \times 4\frac{3}{4}'' \times 12''$. Using a table saw, make a $\frac{5}{16}''$ wide and $\frac{5}{32}''$ deep groove lengthwise in the center of each piece (Fig. A). Glue the two pieces together, with the grooves making a hole through the length of the lamp standard. After the pieces have been glued, a plug of hardwood approximately $1''$ long is driven in each end of the hole. This provides a solid support for the centers.

2. Mount the piece of stock between centers on the lathe and turn to the required dimensions.

3. Sand thoroughly and finish as desired.

4. Remove the piece from the lathe and lay out the holes for the legs.

5. Bore the holes for the legs.

6. Remove the excess stock from the ends of the standard.

7. If a solid piece of stock was used, bore a $\frac{3}{8}''$ hole through the entire length of the standard to receive the wire. If the glued-up stock was used, bore out the wooden plugs with a $\frac{21}{64}''$ drill.

8. Turn the three legs to required dimensions. Be sure the tenon on each leg fits snugly in the hole in the standard.

9. Sand and finish each leg.

10. Glue the legs into the holes in the standard.

11. Wire the lamp.

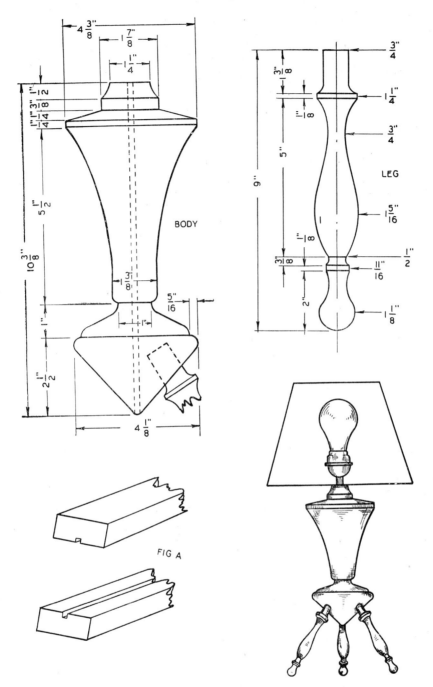

BODY

LEG

FIG A

FIG. 6-29.

127

30. BRIDGE OR FLOOR LAMP

This floor lamp makes a very interesting turned project. The design has been taken from the Greek egg and dart motif. It may be made from any open-grained cabinet wood. This lamp, made from a light-colored wood, filled with a gray or white paste wood filler, and French polished in the lathe, makes an extremely attractive piece of furniture.

Materials Needed:

1 pc., first base:	$2'' \times 12\frac{1}{2}'' \times 12\frac{1}{2}''$	white oak
1 pc., second base:	$2'' \times 10\frac{1}{2}'' \times 10\frac{1}{2}''$	white oak
4 pc., column:	$1\frac{1}{2}'' \times 3'' \times 24''$	white oak
1 length $\frac{1}{8}''$ pipe	$49''$	black
2 lock nuts		

Procedure (see Fig. 6-30):

1. Scribe a $12\frac{1}{2}''$ circle on the first base piece and cut off the corners tangent to the circle. If a band saw is available, cut out the $12''$ circular piece.

2. Plane one face smooth and mount piece on face plate and turn to size and shape (see drawing). It may be necessary to mount the work on the outboard face plate (see Basic Operations).

3. Turn a $3''$ hole through the center of the piece (see drawing). This hole may be cut to within $\frac{1}{16}''$ or $\frac{1}{8}''$ of the steel face plate and the remaining wood cut out by hand after the work has been removed from the face plate.

4. Scribe a $10\frac{1}{4}''$ circle on the second base piece and prepare for turning as in Step 1.

5. Remove the face plate and work from the lathe. Position the second base in the center of the first base and glue and clamp.

6. Remount face plate and work on lathe and turn second base to size and shape (see drawing).

7. Turn a $2''$ dowel hole through the center of the second base.

8. Sand and finish base on lathe. A $\frac{3}{8}''$ hole may now be bored through the side of the base, as indicated on the drawing, to receive the lamp cord.

9. Saw a lengthwise groove, $\frac{7}{16}''$ wide and $\frac{7}{32}''$ deep, on the center line of the face side of all 4 upright pieces.

10. Glue and clamp uprights together face to face. This will make two upright pieces, $3'' \times 3'' \times 24''$ for the column. The $\frac{7}{16}'' \times \frac{7}{16}''$ lengthwise hole will receive the $\frac{1}{8}''$ pipe (O.D. approx. $\frac{3}{8}''$).

11. Make two cardboard templates (see drawing and Basic Operations).

12. Plug the holes in the ends of the bottom upright piece with small pieces of wood. Center and mount piece between centers.

13. Turn bottom upright piece to size and shape. Check egg and dart shapes with templates. A dowel, $2''$ in diameter and $1\frac{3}{4}''$ long, should be turned on the

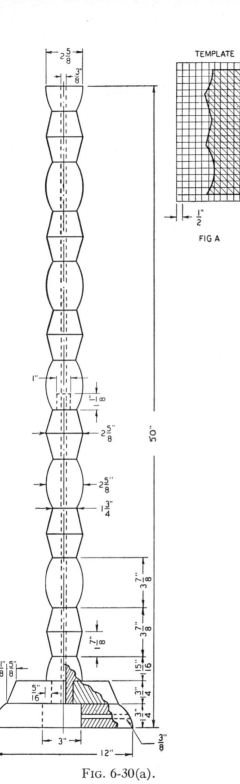

TEMPLATE

FIG A

FIG. 6-30(a).

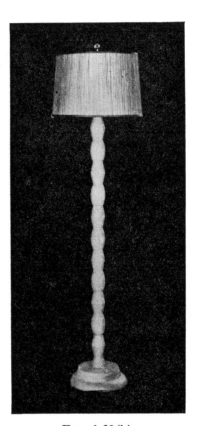

FIG. 6-30(b)

129

bottom of the upright. The shoulder should be turned or trimmed slightly concave. A dowel 1″ in diameter and 1⅛″ long should be turned on the upper end of the upright.

14. Sand and finish in lathe.

15. Prepare and mount second upright between centers as in Step 12.

16. Turn to size and shape (see drawing), using the templates to check correct shapes.

17. With the point of the skew chisel cut a shallow groove 1″ in diameter at the tailstock end of the piece. This groove may be used to help center a 1″ Forstner bit to bore the dowel hole (see drawing).

If a steady rest is available, another method of turning this upright may be used. Mount the work in the lathe using a screw center face plate to drive the work and the tail stock to support the other end. Turn to size and shape. Support the tail stock end of the work piece in a steady rest and remove the tail stock. Operate the lathe at a slow speed and turn bore the 1″ hole 1¼″ deep using the skew chisel.

18. Sand and finish upright.

19. Remove the wooden plugs.

20. Glue and assemble lamp. Before the glue has set insert a 49″ length of ⅛″ black iron pipe, threaded at both ends. Put on lock nuts at each end and pull the assembly together. This pipe strengthens the assembled lamp and provides a sturdy foundation for the heavy lamp fittings.

Index